Raintree Steck-Vaughn

*Illustrated*
# SCIENCE
# ENCYCLOPEDIA

Volume
20

STA – TET

RSVP
RAINTREE
STECK-VAUGHN
P U B L I S H E R S
The Steck-Vaughn Company

*Austin, Texas*

Published by Raintree Steck-Vaughn Publishers, an imprint of
Steck-Vaughn Company.

| | |
|---|---|
| **Executive Editor** | Diane Sharpe |
| **Senior Editor** | Anne Souby |
| **Design Manager** | Joyce Spicer |

This edition edited and designed by Andromeda Oxford Ltd.

**Andromeda Editorial and Design**

| | |
|---|---|
| **Project Manager** | Julia Roles |
| **Editorial Manager** | Jenny Fry |
| **Design** | TT Designs, T&S Truscott |
| **Cover Design** | John Barker |

**Library of Congress Cataloging-in-Publication Data**
Raintree Steck-Vaughn illustrated science encyclopedia.
        p.    cm.
    Includes bibliographical references and index.
    Summary: A twenty-four volume set containing brief articles
on science topics.
    ISBN 0-8172-3943-X (set)
    ISBN 0-8172-3938-3 (Volume 20)
    1. Science—Encyclopedias, Juvenile.   [1. Science—
Encyclopedias.]    I. Raintree Steck-Vaughn Publishers.
Q121.R354      1997
503—dc20                                      96-11078
                                                    CIP
                                                    AC

Printed and Bound in the United States of America.
1 2 3 4 5 6 7 8 9 10 IP 00 99 98 97 96

# USING THE RAINTREE STECK-VAUGHN ILLUSTRATED SCIENCE ENCYCLOPEDIA

You are living in a world in which science, technology, and nature are very important. You see something about science almost every day. It might be on television, in the newspaper, in a book at school, or some other place. Often, you want more information about what you see.

The *Raintree Steck-Vaughn Illustrated Science Encyclopedia* will help you find what you want to know. It contains information on many science subjects. You may want to find out about computers, the environment, space exploration, biology, agriculture, or mathematics, for example. They are all in the *Raintree Steck-Vaughn Illustrated Science Encyclopedia*. There are many, many other subjects covered as well.

There are twenty-four volumes in the encyclopedia. The articles, which are called entries, are in alphabetical order through the first twenty-two volumes. On the spine of each volume, below the volume number, are some letters. The letters above the line are the first three letters of the first entry in that volume. The letters below the line are the first three letters of the last entry in that volume. In Volume 1, for example, you see that the first entry begins with **AAR** and that the last entry begins with **ANT**. Using the letters makes it easy to find the volume you need.

In Volume 23, there are three special features—reference charts and tables, a bibliography, and an index. In Volume 24, there are interesting projects that you can do on your own. The projects are fun to do, and they help you discover and understand important science principles. Many can give you ideas that can help you develop your own science fair projects.

**Main Entries** There are two kinds of main entries in the *Raintree Steck-Vaughn Illustrated Science Encyclopedia*. Many of the entries are major topics that are spread over several pages. The titles of these entries are shown at the top of the page in a yellow box. Other entries required less space to cover the topic fully. The titles of these main entries are printed in capital letters. They look like this: **ABALONE**. At the beginning of some entries, you will see a phonetic pronunciation of the entry title, such as (ăb′ ə lō′ nē).

In the front of each volume, there is a pronunciation key. Use it the same way you use your dictionary's pronunciation key.

**Cross-References** Within the main entries are cross-references referring to other entries in the encyclopedia. Within an entry, they look like this: (see MAMMAL). At the end of an entry, they look like this: *See also* HYENA. These cross-references tell you where to find other helpful information on the subject you are reading about.

**Projects** At the end of some entries, you will see this symbol: PROJECT 1. It tells you which projects related to that entry are in Volume 24.

**Illustrations** There are thousands of photographs, drawings, graphs, diagrams, tables, and other illustrations in the *Raintree Steck-Vaughn Illustrated Science Encyclopedia*. They will help you better understand the entries you read. Captions describe the illustrations. Many of the illustrations also have labels that point out important parts.

**Activities** Some main entries include activities presented in a special box. These activities are short projects that give you a chance to work with science on your own.

**Index** In Volume 23, the index lists every main entry by volume and page number. Many subjects that are not main entries are also listed in the index, as well as the illustrations, projects, activities, and reference charts and tables.

**Bibliography** In Volume 23, there is also a bibliography for students. The books in this list are on a variety of topics and can supplement what you have learned in the *Raintree Steck-Vaughn Illustrated Science Encyclopedia*.

The *Raintree Steck-Vaughn Illustrated Science Encyclopedia* was designed especially for you, the student. It is a source of knowledge for the world of science, technology, and nature. Enjoy it!

# PRONUNCIATION KEY

Each symbol has the same sound as the darker letters in the sample words.

| | | | | | |
|---|---|---|---|---|---|
| ə | balloon, ago | îr | deer, pier | r | root, tire |
| ă | map, have | j | join, germ | s | so, press |
| ā | day, made | k | king, ask | sh | shoot, machine |
| âr | care, bear | l | let, cool | t | to, stand |
| ä | father, car | m | man, same | th | thin, death |
| b | ball, rib | n | no, turn | *th* | then, this |
| ch | choose, nature | ng | bring, long | ŭ | up, cut |
| d | did, add | ŏ | odd, pot | ûr | urge, hurt |
| ĕ | bell, get | ō | cone, know | v | view, give |
| ē | sweet, easy | ô | all, saw | w | wood, glowing |
| f | fan, soft | oi | boy, boil | y | yes, year |
| g | good, big | ou | now, loud | z | zero, raise |
| h | hurt, ahead | ŏŏ | good, took | zh | leisure, vision |
| ĭ | rip, ill | ōō | boot, noon | ′ | strong accent |
| ī | side, sky | p | part, scrap | ˏ | weak accent |

# GUIDE TO MEASUREMENT ABBREVIATIONS

All measurements in the *Raintree Steck-Vaughn Illustrated Science Encyclopedia* are given in both the customary system and the metric system [in brackets like these]. Following are the abbreviations used for various units of measure.

## Customary Units of Measure

| | |
|---|---|
| mi. = miles | cu. yd. = cubic yards |
| m.p.h. = miles per hour | cu. ft. = cubic feet |
| yd. = yards | cu. in. = cubic inches |
| ft. = feet | gal. = gallons |
| in. = inches | pt. = pints |
| sq. mi. = square miles | qt. = quarts |
| sq. yd. = square yards | lb. = pounds |
| sq. ft. = square feet | oz. = ounces |
| sq. in. = square inches | fl. oz. = fluid ounces |
| cu. mi. = cubic miles | °F = degrees Fahrenheit |

## Metric Units of Measure

| | |
|---|---|
| km = kilometers | cu. km = cubic kilometers |
| kph = kilometers per hour | cu. m = cubic meters |
| m = meters | cu. cm = cubic centimeters |
| cm = centimeters | ml = milliliters |
| mm = millimeters | kg = kilograms |
| sq. km = square kilometers | g = grams |
| sq. m = square meters | mg = milligrams |
| sq. cm = square centimeters | °C = degrees Celsius |

For information on how to convert customary measurements to metric measurements, see the Metric Conversions table in Volume 23.

A star is a huge sphere of glowing gas in space. Stars range in size from stars smaller than the earth to stars that are hundreds of times the size of our sun (see EARTH; SPACE; SUN).

Except for the sun, stars are not usually visible from the earth during the day. On a clear night, however, many stars of different brightness can be observed. About five thousand stars are visible from the earth without the aid of a telescope (see TELESCOPE). There are, however, many trillions of stars in the universe (see UNIVERSE). Most of these stars are too distant for us to see. The distance of stars from the earth is unimaginably huge. The distance to stars other than the sun is measured in light-years. A light-year is the distance that light travels in one year. One light-year equals 5.88 trillion mi. [9.46 trillion km] (see LIGHT-YEAR).

For centuries, people have been fascinated by the stars. They have named groups of stars according to the shapes or patterns they seem to make. These groups are called constellations (see CONSTELLATION). A large group of stars is called a galaxy (see GALAXY).

**Characteristics of stars** Stars vary considerably in diameter, color, temperature, distance from the earth, and luminosity (brightness). The five major categories of stars based on diameter are supergiant, giant, medium-sized (or dwarf), white dwarf, and neutron stars (see DWARF STAR; GIANT STAR; NEUTRON STAR; WHITE DWARF). Supergiants may have diameters that are several hundred times larger than that of the sun. Two famous supergiants are Antares and Betelgeuse. Giant stars have diameters that are about ten times to one hundred times the diameter of the sun. Medium-sized stars are about the same size as the sun. More specifically, their diameters may be about one-tenth to ten times the diameter of the sun. White dwarfs are very small stars. Neutron stars are the tiniest of all stars. They have a diameter of only about 6 mi. [10 km].

The color of a star indicates its surface temperature. The hottest stars are blue. Blue stars may have temperatures of 40,000°F [22,000°C]. Red stars are the coolest, with temperatures of about 3,200°F

[1,760°C]. The temperatures indicated by other colors, such as white and yellow, are between the temperatures indicated by blue and red. Stars of all sizes vary in temperature. For example, some giant stars are blue, meaning they are extremely hot. Other giant stars have a reddish color, indicating a much lower temperature. The sun is a yellow star.

The closest star to earth, the sun, is about 93 million mi. [150 million km] from the earth. Proxima Centauri, the closest star to the sun, is 4.3 light-years away from Earth.

The luminosity of a star is called its magnitude. Apparent (or visual) magnitude is the brightness of a star as seen from Earth. Absolute magnitude is the brightness a star would have if it were 32.6 light-years (10 parsecs) from Earth (see MAGNITUDE; PARSEC). The sun has an apparent magnitude of

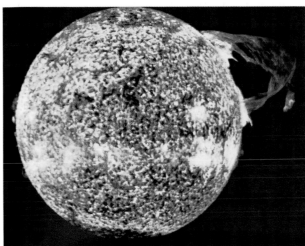

**FORMATION AND FLARES**

The satellite photograph (top) shows a "newborn" star (the red patch indicated by the white arrow). This star has not reached the point at which fusion occurs. When it does, the star will give off heat and light. Like our sun, it may throw out huge flares (bottom).

-27.0 and an absolute magnitude of 4.8. The brightest star, Sirius, has an apparent magnitude of -1.4 and an absolute magnitude of 1.3. Other very bright stars include Canopus, Arcturus, Vega, Capella, Rigel, Procyon, Betelgeuse, Achernar, Beta Centauri, Altair, Alpha Crucis, Aldebaran, Spica, and Antares.

## Special kinds of stars

There are several kinds of stars in the universe that have special characteristics. Scientists are collecting information to learn more about these stars. For example, a variable star is a star that shines dimly, then brightly, then dimly again. A kind of variable star called a pulsating variable star expands and contracts at regular intervals. The brightness of the pulsating variable star varies with its expansion and contraction. The time between the star's expansions is called its period. The periods of pulsating variables range from a few hours to an indefinite period of time (see VARIABLE STAR).

Another kind of variable star, called a nova, becomes bright due to an explosion (see NOVA). The increased brightness may last for days or months before the star returns to its original brightness. The most brilliant exploding stars are called supernovae (plural of *supernova*). A supernova explosion observed in 1054 produced the Crab Nebula (see CRAB NEBULA; SUPERNOVA). A giant supernova was observed in a galaxy near Earth in 1987. This was the nearest supernova to Earth since the invention of the telescope.

Another example of a star that has special characteristics is a pulsar. Pulsars are stars that emit electromagnetic radiation, such as radio waves, at regular intervals (see ELECTROMAGNETIC RADIATION; PULSAR).

## Energy production in a star

Hydrogen and helium are the main elements in stars. However, stars contain small amounts of certain other elements (see ELEMENT; HELIUM; HYDROGEN). Stars can be analyzed according to the elements they contain. In order to analyze the elements, astronomers study the spectrum of light received from the star (see SPECTROSCOPE; SPECTRUM).

Most stars produce energy by changing hydrogen to helium. This process is known as nuclear fusion (see FUSION). In stars that undergo nuclear fusion, hydrogen atoms in the core of the star collide. The nuclei (plural of *nucleus*) of the atoms join to form helium. A small amount of matter is converted to a huge amount of energy during fusion (see ATOM; NUCLEUS).

## The life cycle of a star

The life cycle of a star is a very complex process. Essentially, however, astronomers think that a star forms originally from a cloud of gas and dust called a nebula (see NEBULA). Scientists think that eventually the cloud forms into the shape of a ball. This process may take millions of years. The ball gets smaller as gravity draws in more material and pressure increases (see GRAVITY). After some time, the temperature at the core (center) reaches about 2,000,000°F [1,100,000°C]. This high temperature causes the fusion of hydrogen to form helium. The energy released by this reaction heats up the outer portion of the ball. The gas begins to glow, and a star is born.

A star continues producing energy until most of its hydrogen has been converted into helium. When the hydrogen

Hydrogen burning

**Medium-sized star**

**Protostar, or "newborn" star**

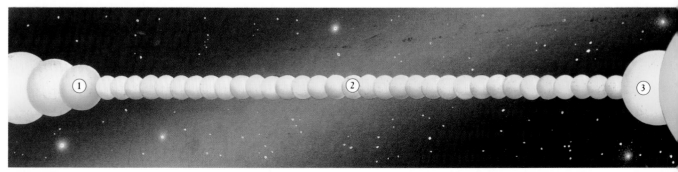

supply in the star's core decreases to a certain point, the star contracts. This causes the core to become hotter, while the surface becomes cooler. The star expands and becomes a red giant. What happens next depends on the mass (amount of matter) of the star. Stars with about the same mass as the sun lose their outer layers of gas and then collapse inward, forming a white dwarf star. White dwarf stars shine faintly for billions of years. Stars that are more massive than the sun go from being red giants to supergiants. In time, they may explode and become supernovae.

Even after they explode, some supernovae still have a great deal of mass at their cores. These stars may then collapse in upon themselves because of this large mass. If the supernova's core has less than 2.5 times but more than 1.4 times the mass of the sun, the supernova will develop into a neutron star. If the supernova's core has more than 2.5 times the mass of the sun, a black hole will result. Black holes are so dense that no light can escape their gravitational fields. That is why they are called black holes (see BLACK HOLE).

Astronomers still have much to learn about stars. Phenomena such as pulsars and black holes are not clearly understood. By understanding the process of how stars form and die, scientists may someday have a better understanding of the sun and its solar system, as well as of the vast Milky Way galaxy.

*See also* COSMOLOGY; MILKY WAY; SOLAR SYSTEM.

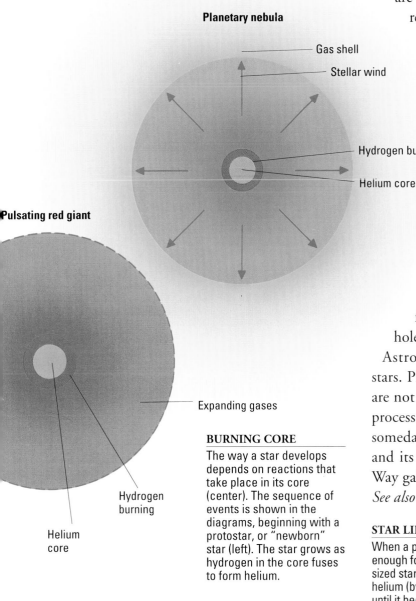

**Planetary nebula**

Gas shell

Stellar wind

Hydrogen burning

Helium core

**Pulsating red giant**

Expanding gases

Hydrogen burning

Helium core

### BURNING CORE

The way a star develops depends on reactions that take place in its core (center). The sequence of events is shown in the diagrams, beginning with a protostar, or "newborn" star (left). The star grows as hydrogen in the core fuses to form helium.

### STAR LIFE CYCLE

When a protostar, or "newborn" star, (1 below, far left) gets hot enough for hydrogen fusion to begin, it becomes a medium-sized star (2), similar to our sun. As hydrogen is turned into helium (by the fusion process), the star begins to expand (3) until it becomes a red giant (4). Helium also undergoes fusion, and as it is used up, the star begins to collapse (5), forming a planetary nebula (cloud of gas) (6) and a white dwarf star (7).

**STARCH—Source**
Starch comes from plants. Much of the starch we eat comes from cereal crops, such as barley, rice, rye, wheat, and (left) corn.

**STARCH—Uses**
Seeds of rye and wheat are ground into flour and used to make high-energy foods such as bread, cakes, and pasta. Rice is generally eaten whole and not made into flour.

**STARCH** Starch is a soft white powder that comes from living plants. It is a carbohydrate, made up of carbon, hydrogen, and oxygen. Starch is formed in plants from sugars made during the process of photosynthesis (see CARBOHYDRATE; PHOTOSYNTHESIS). Starch is one of our most important nutrients. It is a source of body energy. Starch is found in corn, potatoes, rice, wheat, and many other foods (see NUTRITION).

Starch changes chemically in the digestive system (see DIGESTIVE SYSTEM). In digestion, starch is broken down into sugars that can be absorbed into the bloodstream (see SUGAR).

Starch does not dissolve in water, alcohol, or ether. It does form a thick paste when mixed with water and is sometimes used to glue paper together. Starch is also commonly used to stiffen textiles, such as shirt collars.

**STARFISH** Starfish are not fish, but echinoderms (see ECHINODERMATA). They are related to such sea animals as brittle stars, sea urchins, and sea cucumbers. Starfish live in all oceans and are especially abundant in the northwest Pacific.

Starfish usually have five pointed arms radiating from a central body. Some starfish have as many as forty arms. The animals are usually orange or red in color. The upper skin of a starfish is spiny. The spines are made up of lime, which develops from parts of the skeleton just under the skin.

The mouth of a starfish is located on the bottom surface of its central body. The undersides of the arms have many water-filled tubes called tube feet, which are used to walk along the ocean floor. Starfish also use the tube feet to pry open the shells of bivalves, their main food (see BIVALVE). When feeding, the starfish pushes its stomach out of its mouth and into the bivalve. It then digests the bivalve. Starfish are serious pests in oyster farms and in mussel beds. A large starfish called the crown-of-thorns has destroyed large areas of

**STARFISH**

Starfish are not fish, but members of the group of invertebrates (animals without backbones) called echinoderms. Some starfish have very short arms (left) and resemble their relatives the sand dollars. Most starfish have from five to as many as forty arms (bottom right). Slender members of the group are known as brittle stars (bottom left).

Australia's Great Barrier Reef by eating the corals.

Starfish are eaten by fish, crustaceans, and shore birds. Sometimes, starfish escape from their enemies by breaking off an arm that is in the enemy's grasp. Starfish have remarkable powers of regeneration and can grow a new arm to replace the lost one (see REGENERATION). Even if a starfish is cut into two pieces, each of the pieces can develop into a new individual.

**STARLING** A starling is a dark, fat-bodied bird that belongs to the family Sturnidae. It has a short tail; long, narrow bill; and shades of dull purple and green on its breast. In winter, its plumage is heavily speckled with white. The starling is native to Europe. It was brought to North America and is now widespread throughout the continent. Starlings often nest in holes that they forcefully take over from other birds. Flocks of starlings in the midwestern United States are so large that they damage crops and trees. Their droppings also damage the buildings on which the birds roost at night. These flocks also can create a health hazard, because they carry and spread diseases. Scientists and the U.S. Army have begun campaigns to reduce the numbers of starlings in areas where the birds are a problem.

STARLING

Starlings are native to Europe. However, they have become abundant in North America. Flocks of starlings can be so large that they damage crops, trees, and buildings.

**STATES OF MATTER** States of matter are the various forms that a substance can have. There are three states in which matter commonly exists. They are solid, liquid, and gas (see GAS; LIQUID; SOLID). Depending on the temperature and pressure, every substance takes one of these forms. One form may change into another if the temperature and/or pressure is sufficiently changed. For example, water can be turned into solid ice by cooling or into steam by heating. The gases in the air can be liquefied by cooling and compressing them. Mercury can be changed into a solid metal by cooling it (see PRESSURE; TEMPERATURE).

Solids, liquids, and gases are different because of the different energy that their atoms or molecules have (see ATOM; MOLECULE). In solids, the atoms or molecules are tightly held together. This gives the solid a certain shape. The atoms or molecules have little energy to move, though they can vibrate (move from side to side) around fixed positions.

In liquids, the atoms or molecules have more energy and can move more freely. The liquid can easily change shape. In gases, the atoms or molecules have much more energy. The atoms and molecules move about without any certain pattern. Liquids and gases are sometimes grouped together as fluids, because their particles can flow, or move past one another freely.

When a solid—or a liquid or gas—is heated, extra energy is added to its particles, and they vibrate more. If sufficient heat is used, the particles will vibrate so strongly that the forces keeping the solid in a certain shape are overcome. Eventually, the particles move so freely that the solid liquefies. More heat gives the particles even more energy, and a gas is formed.

Extreme heating gives so much energy to the particles of a gas that several things happen. First of all, molecules break down into atoms. Then, the electrons leave their atoms. The electrons and the nuclei of the atoms move about separately. This forms a plasma, which is a fourth state of matter (see PLASMA (PHYSICS)). The interior of the sun is composed of plasma. **PROJECT 15**

# STATISTICS

Statistics is the collection, sorting, and interpreting of large amounts of information. The information is usually in numerical form. Statistics may summarize the findings of a biologist, world trade figures, the sales of detergents, or data (information) from almost any field.

Statistical information can be shown in a number of ways. Bar graphs, circle graphs (or pie charts), picture graphs (or isotype diagrams or pictograms), charts, and tables are commonly used (see GRAPH). For example, the table below shows how a sample of 100 people prefer to spend their leisure time.

| Theater | Watching TV | Sports | Total |
|---------|-------------|--------|-------|
| 11 | 65 | 24 | 100 |

To show this on a circle graph, a circle is divided in proportion to the figures. The circle graph below was based on data from the table.

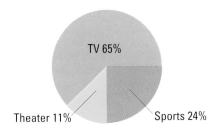

A pie chart (below) is a three-dimensional version of a circle graph.

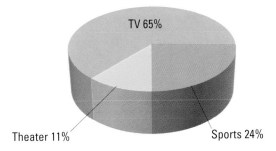

In a picture graph, a symbol is used to represent each item, or each 10 items, or whatever number is most useful. In this case, one symbol is used to represent 10 people.

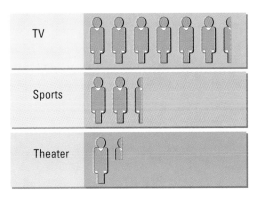

If the information can be sorted into numerical groups, and the number occurring in each group is recorded, this is called a frequency distribution. For example, the table below shows the number of peas in each pod from a sample of 40 pods.

| Number of peas per pod | 1 | 2 | 3 | 4 | 5 | 6 | 7 | 8 | Total |
|------------------------|---|---|---|---|---|---|---|---|-------|
| Number of pods (frequency) | 3 | 4 | 6 | 7 | 8 | 6 | 4 | 2 | 40 |

A bar graph can be used to illustrate the frequency distribution. This type of graph is often called a histogram.

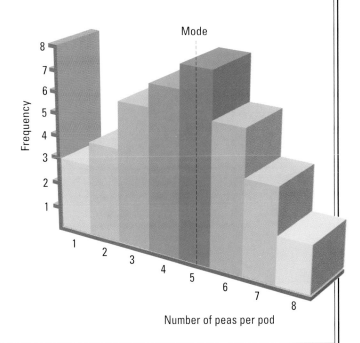

The largest group in the bar graph is called the mode (see MEAN, MEDIAN, AND MODE). In the above example, the mode is 5. The mode, then, is the value that occurs most often in the set.

The most familiar kind of average is the mean. To find the mean of a set of numbers, first find the total and then divide by the total frequency. The total number of peas in the above example is found by multiplying the number of peas per pod by the number of pods in each group. The calculation is shown below.

| No. of peas per pod (X) | No. of pods (frequency) (f) | Total no. of peas (fX) |
|---|---|---|
| 1 | 3 | 1 x 3 = 3 |
| 2 | 4 | 2 x 4 = 8 |
| 3 | 6 | 3 x 6 = 18 |
| 4 | 7 | 4 x 7 = 28 |
| 5 | 8 | 5 x 8 = 40 |
| 6 | 6 | 6 x 6 = 36 |
| 7 | 4 | 7 x 4 = 28 |
| 8 | 2 | 8 x 2 = 16 |
| Totals | 40 | 177 |

The mean number of peas per pod is 177 divided by 40, or 4.425.

The middle value is called the median. One way to find the median is to draw a cumulative frequency table. To do this, count the frequency up to and including each value. Below is a cumulative frequency table.

| No. of peas per pod (X) | No. of pods (frequency) (f) | Cumulative frequency (cf) |
|---|---|---|
| 1 | 3 | 3 |
| 2 | 4 | 7 (= 3 + 4) |
| 3 | 6 | 13 (= 7 + 6) |
| 4 | 7 | 20 |
| 5 | 8 | 28 |
| 6 | 6 | 34 |
| 7 | 4 | 38 |
| 8 | 2 | 40 |
| Totals | 40 | 183 |

The median is 183 divided by 40, or approximately 4.5. The graph of this distribution is shown below.

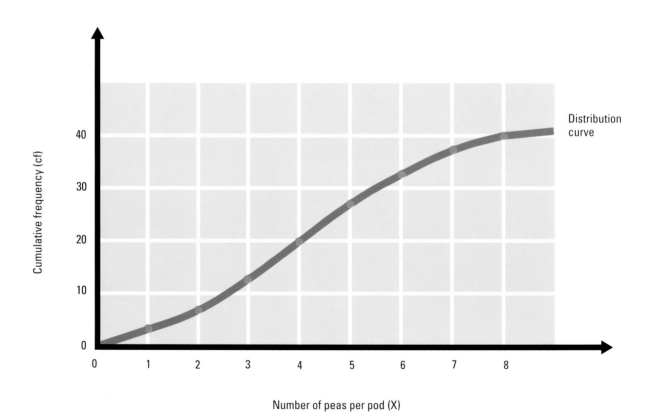

Distribution curve

Cumulative frequency (cf)

Number of peas per pod (X)

If continuously variable quantities, such as heights of persons or scores of intelligence tests, are plotted on a graph, a normal distribution curve is obtained.

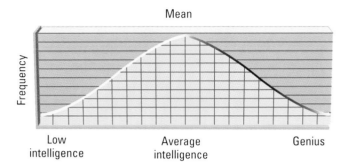

Mean

Low intelligence     Average intelligence     Genius

This curve is a smoothed-out histogram. This graph shows that, in any population, more persons of average intelligence occur than people with low intelligence or geniuses. This is obvious, but the normal curve shows at once how many of each occur. Normal curves can be high or flat, depending on the range of variation, or "dispersion," of the characteristic being measured. For example, the intensities of light given out by electric light bulbs vary much more than the lifetime of the bulbs before they burn out. Notice, however, that most bulbs burn for an average period, giving out an average amount of light.

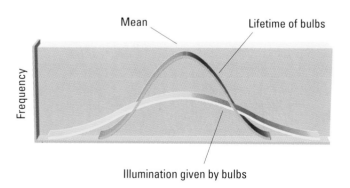

Mean     Lifetime of bulbs

Illumination given by bulbs

Such graphs can be used, for example, to estimate how many bulbs could be expected to burn for 200 hours, with a particular light intensity. However, statisticians do not have to draw graphs to make such estimates. Having obtained the necessary sample of data,

they can arrive at the answer directly by using statistical tables.

If two sets of data for a particular sample are associated (related), it is useful to show them on another kind of graph. The table below gives the grades obtained by 9 students in 20-point quizzes in science and mathematics.

| Student | A | B | C | D | E | F | G | H | I |
|---|---|---|---|---|---|---|---|---|---|
| Grade in science | 18 | 15 | 19 | 13 | 16 | 8 | 7 | 15 | 10 |
| Grade in math | 20 | 17 | 18 | 14 | 15 | 9 | 5 | 16 | 12 |

The scatter diagram below is drawn by making one peg for each student. The pegs are made as high up as the students' math grades along one axis and as far out as the science grades along the other.

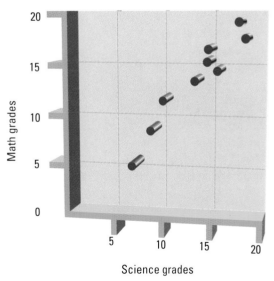

Science grades

The diagram suggests that a student who is good at science is usually also good at mathematics. In this case, it can be said that there is good correlation between the two sets of grades.

It is easy to make statistics misleading. Sometimes correlations between different sets of data prove to be false on closer examination. Statisticians need to examine their data thoroughly and consider all explanations for correlations before drawing conclusions.

# STEAM ENGINE

A steam engine is a device that is powered by steam and is capable of doing work. The first device to be driven by steam is said to be the rotating sphere called an aeolipile, invented by Hero of Alexandria in the first century A.D. Steam under pressure escaped from the sphere through small jets set at angles, driving the sphere around on its axle. It was not until the sixteenth century that a steam engine with a more general application was invented.

The steam engine is an external combustion engine (see ENGINE). This means that fuel is combusted, or burned, outside the cylinder that produces power. The first practical steam engine was invented by Thomas Savery in 1698. It had a boiler from which steam passed through a pipe to a cylinder. The cylinder was connected to other pipes and valves. When the cylinder had been filled with steam, it was cooled from the outside with water. The steam condensed and created a vacuum, which sucked water up through the pipes and past the

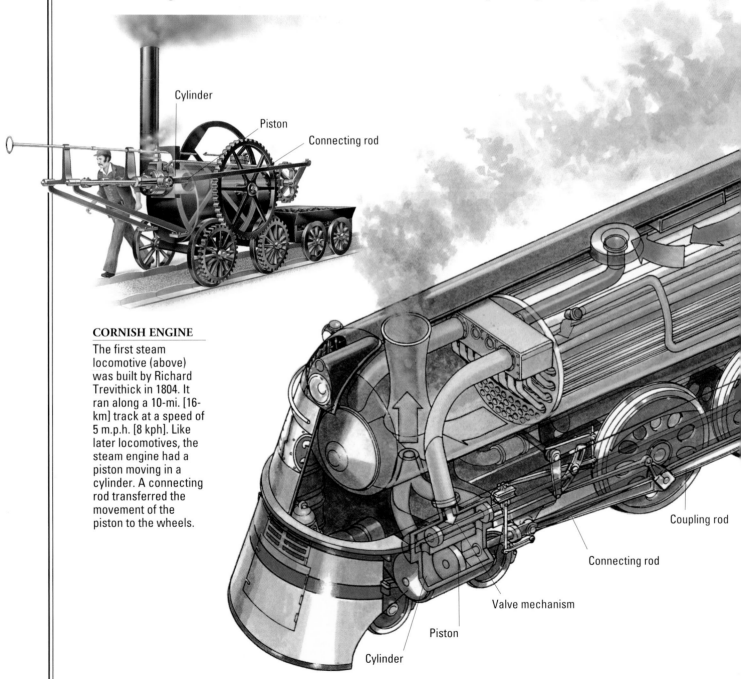

Cylinder

Piston

Connecting rod

**CORNISH ENGINE**
The first steam locomotive (above) was built by Richard Trevithick in 1804. It ran along a 10-mi. [16-km] track at a speed of 5 m.p.h. [8 kph]. Like later locomotives, the steam engine had a piston moving in a cylinder. A connecting rod transferred the movement of the piston to the wheels.

Coupling rod

Connecting rod

Valve mechanism

Piston

Cylinder

valves (see CONDENSATION; VACUUM). This type of steam engine served as a type of water pump.

In 1712, Thomas Newcomen developed an improved steam engine. The steam was cooled by a jet of water sprayed into the cylinder. The cylinder contained a piston. The piston was pushed up by the steam pressure from the boiler and then down again when the steam condensed and pulled it toward the vacuum. The piston was attached to one end of a beam that was balanced at the middle. The other end of the beam was attached to a pump. The pump was powered by the pistons moving up and down. Newcomen engines were used to pump water out of mine shafts.

### DRIVING GEAR

The combination of rods, valves, and pistons on a steam locomotive (left) is known as the driving gear. In the set-up shown in the diagram below, the valve mechanism has opened the rear port to allow steam to enter the cylinder behind the piston. Steam pressure forces the piston forward, pulling the connecting rod and rotating the driving axle by means of a crank. The coupling rod transfers the rotary movement to the other driving wheels of the locomotive.

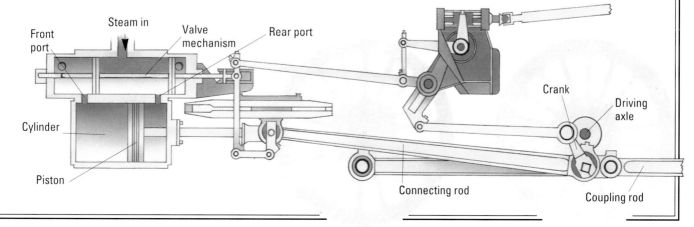

Front port
Steam in
Valve mechanism
Rear port
Cylinder
Piston
Crank
Driving axle
Connecting rod
Coupling rod

James Watt was a Scottish engineer who improved the steam engine (see WATT, JAMES). In 1769, Watt took out his first patent for an improved model. (A patent is a document issued by a government. It grants a person exclusive rights to an invention for a period of time.) His engine had a cylinder with a piston that moved from side to side. The cylinder had two holes in the side, called the ports. The ports were connected alternately to the steam from the boiler and to the exhaust.

The steam was fed first to one side of the piston and then the other. This is known as the double-action principle. The pressure of steam drove the piston back and forth. There was no need to cool the cylinder to cause a suction effect. The cylinder was kept permanently hot. It was insulated with packing material for extra efficiency.

The piston was connected to a drive shaft. This shaft was connected to valves. As the drive shaft moved, the valves opened and closed the ports. The amount that the valves moved each time could be controlled. This determined the amount of steam that entered the cylinder to drive the piston. The power supplied by the engine depended on the amount of steam admitted on each stroke, or movement of the piston. Watt's engines ran at a fairly low pressure (about 7 lb. per sq. in.) [0.5 kg per sq. cm].

The drive shaft of Watt's engine could be connected to any number of machines, allowing the engine to power the machine. Watt's engine had a great effect on the Industrial Revolution in the following years. Factories were no longer tied down to riverside sites where water mills were used. They could be in places convenient for raw materials and transport.

The steam engine greatly changed transportation. The Cornish engine, developed by Richard Trevithick, had a boiler heated by hot gases carried through tubes from a coal fire. This was the first type of high-pressure steam engine. It drove the first locomotive, which was first used on December 24, 1804 (see LOCOMOTIVE).

By the end of the nineteenth century, efficient engines for railway locomotives and ships were working at much higher pressures (up to 200 lb. per sq. in.) [14 kg per sq. cm]. This meant a much more efficient use of steam. High pressures required superheated steam, with very high temperatures in the boiler. This led to the development of new materials and designs to withstand the high temperatures.

Today, most of the functions of steam engines have been taken over by internal combustion engines, fueled by gasoline or diesel oil. However, steam is used to generate electricity. The steam may be produced by heating with coal, oil, natural gas, or nuclear power. The kind of steam engine that is used does not have cylinders. It is generally a steam turbine (see TURBINE). The steam turbine was invented by Sir Charles Parsons. Steam turbines can handle steam at higher pressures than piston engines can, and they are more compact than piston engines of similar power.

**TRACTION ENGINE**

During the 1800s, steam engines called traction engines were used on farms to pull plows and power agricultural machinery. Tractors with diesel or gasoline engines have now replaced steam traction engines.

Steel is an alloy of iron and carbon. Other metals are added to give steel special properties (see ALLOY; CARBON; IRON). Steel is one of the most widely used and least expensive metals ever developed. It is used in automobiles, skyscrapers, frying pans, safety pins, and thousands of other objects—including almost every kind of machine. In the United States alone, more than 143 million tons [130 million metric tons] of steel are produced every year.

There are three basic types of steels: carbon, low-alloy, and high-alloy. Carbon steel is made of iron and a small amount of carbon—usually less than one percent. Any other elements in carbon steel are usually considered to be impurities. More than 90 percent of all steel used in industry is carbon steel. The carbon in carbon steel is in the form of a compound called cementite ($Fe_3C$). The more cementite the steel contains, the greater its strength and hardness.

Low-alloy steels are like carbon steel except that they also contain from 1 to 5 percent added elements. The elements most commonly added to the alloy are chromium, molybdenum, nickel, titanium, tungsten, vanadium, or a combination of two or more of these elements. Low-alloy steels are very strong and are used in construction, in aircraft landing gear, and in machines that are subjected to great stress.

High-alloy steels contain more than 5 percent added elements such as chromium, manganese, molybdenum, or tungsten. These steels usually have special properties such as resistance to corrosion or heat (see CORROSION). High-alloy steels are used in tools, kitchenware, and jet engines. The stainless steels are high-alloy steels (see STAINLESS STEEL). If an alloy contains less than 50 percent iron, however, it is considered to be a ferro-alloy instead of steel.

**Steel production** Carbon steel was first produced several thousand years ago by melting iron ore over a charcoal fire. When some of the carbon from the charcoal alloyed with the iron, carbon steel was formed. Because this was an expensive and impractical way to make steel, iron remained the most commonly used metal. In the mid-1800s, a process was developed that made it easier and cheaper to produce steel. Known as the Bessemer process, it involved blowing air through molten iron to help burn off and remove impurities (see BESSEMER, SIR HENRY).

In the late 1800s, the open hearth and electric furnace processes were developed. These were especially important because, for the first time, scrap (leftover) steel and scrap iron could be reused to produce steel. The open hearth furnace reaches a

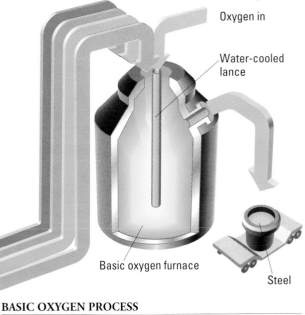

**BASIC OXYGEN PROCESS**

A basic oxygen furnace for steel making is charged with molten (melted) pig iron, scrap steel, and lime. For special steels, other metals may also be added. Oxygen is injected at high speed through a water-cooled pipe called a lance to burn off carbon. Other impurities combine with the lime to form slag.

**IRON FOR STEEL**

The chief component of steel is iron, shown here being run off from the base of a blast furnace.

temperature of about 3,000°F [1,600°C] and can produce as much as 220 tons [200 metric tons] of steel every eight hours. An electric furnace is heated to about 3,500°F [1,900°C] and can produce about 88 tons [80 metric tons] of steel each day.

The Bessemer, open hearth, and electric furnace processes produced enough steel at low enough cost that steel soon replaced iron as the most widely used metal. Although these processes are still in use, most steel today is produced in the basic oxygen furnace. This furnace uses a process similar to the Bessemer process, except that pure oxygen is blown through the molten iron at very high speeds. This burns away impurities and excess carbon. With another charge in the furnace, superheated steam may also be added to the molten (melted) iron to help remove impurities. These burned impurities rise to the top of the molten iron and are removed, leaving pure carbon steel. The molten steel may then be removed from the furnace and mixed with certain elements to produce the desired alloy.

This steel alloy can be poured into molds to form ingots (see INGOT). In this form, the steel can be stored, transported, or processed further using various heat treatments to improve its properties.

In quenching, steel is heated to a very high temperature and then quenched, or cooled rapidly, in water or oil. The steel can then be tempered by reheating it to a carefully controlled lower temperature and quenching it again. Tempered steel is very strong. Annealing is a heat treatment process in which the steel is not quenched but is allowed to cool slowly. Annealed steel is softer and more easily shaped than is tempered steel (see ANNEALING). Case-hardened steel has a hardened surface that is produced by adding carbon during the heat treatment.

Throughout the steel-making process, samples of the steel are removed and tested. Using spectroscopes, X rays, and electron microscopes, specialists can determine and control the quality of the steel being produced (see ELECTRON MICROSCOPE; SPECTROSCOPE; X RAY). These samples are also tested to determine such properties of the steel as its elasticity and ability to withstand stress (see ELASTICITY; STRESS AND STRAIN). The finalized steel is then poured into ingots; rolled into sheets, bars, or other shapes; cast into small molds to form billets (bars) or slabs; or otherwise shaped for use in industry. *See also* METAL AND METALLURGY.

# STEINMETZ, CHARLES PROTEUS
(1865–1923) (stīn' mĕts, chärlz prō' tē əs) Charles Proteus Steinmetz was a mathematician and electrical engineer who made many contributions to the understanding and use of electricity (see ELECTRICITY). He was born Karl August Steinmetz in Germany. He entered the University of Breslau in Germany (now Wroclaw, Poland) at age seventeen. There, he was nicknamed Proteus after a figure in Roman mythology who had many talents. Fearing imprisonment because of his anti-government political beliefs, Steinmetz fled to Switzerland in 1888. There, he received his doctorate in mathematics. In 1889, Steinmetz moved to the United States. Soon afterward, he changed his name.

Steinmetz began working for the General Electric Company several years later and continued to work for them throughout his career. It was at General Electric that Steinmetz developed many of his theories. For example, Steinmetz refined the existing theory of alternating electric current, allowing engineers to measure and better control the alternating current coming from power plants. Steinmetz also explained the delay that occurs when alternating current switches direction (see ALTERNATING CURRENT; CURRENT, ELECTRIC). The delay, called hysteresis, caused electric motors and generators to burn out quickly (see ELECTRIC MOTOR; GENERATOR, ELECTRICAL). Steinmetz's explanation led to the development of more durable generators and motors. Steinmetz also improved the electrical transformer (see TRANSFORMER). He also developed the first efficient system of electric street lights.

Steinmetz wrote many articles and books on electricity and received patents for nearly two hundred inventions. A patent is a document issued by a government. It grants a person exclusive rights to an invention for a period of time.

# STELE (stē'lē) The stele is that part of a plant root or stem that contains the xylem, phloem, and endodermis (see PHLOEM; ROOT; STEM; XYLEM). Xylem and phloem are vascular tissues that carry plant food and water between the roots and the leaves (see VASCULAR PLANT). The endodermis is a layer of thickened cells around the outside of the vascular tissues. The stele can be in one bundle in the center of the stem or root or in several parallel bundles. In either case, it is surrounded by the cortex.

*See also* CORTEX.

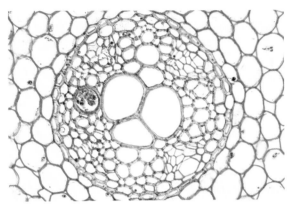

**STELE**

In this illustration of stele, which shows a cross section as viewed from above, the xylem is arranged in a kind of cross in the center, and the phloem (green) is in between the lengths of the cross.

# STEM The stem is the part of a plant that usually grows aboveground in an upright position. It has two main functions: support and transport. It supports the leaves and reproductive structures (flowers or cones) and displays them so that the leaves receive optimum amounts of light and the flowers are well exposed to insects or wind. It transports water and dissolved minerals from the roots to the leaves and dissolved food from the leaves to the roots.

**Structure** The tip of the stem is the terminal bud. This bud produces a hormone called auxin (see HORMONE). Auxin controls the growth of the lateral (side) buds. Inside the terminal bud is rapidly dividing meristem tissue (see MERISTEM). This meristem is responsible for most of the stem's growth. Some of these meristem cells become longer and begin to specialize to perform various functions (see DIFFERENTIATION, CELLULAR). The outermost of these cells form the epidermis. Some form buds, which grow into leaves or flowers (see FLOWER; LEAF). The point of leaf attachment is a swollen area on the stem called a node. The part of the stem between two nodes is an internode (see

NODE). In many plants, some of the outer cells die and become cork. Cork helps waterproof and protect the stem (see BARK; CORK).

The cells near the center of the stem specialize into transport, or vascular, tissue (see VASCULAR PLANT). Some develop into xylem for transporting water and dissolved minerals (see XYLEM). Some develop into phloem for transporting dissolved food (see PHLOEM). In young dicotyledonous plants, the xylem and phloem form a ring of vascular bundles. Each bundle has xylem on the inside and phloem on the outside, with a band of cambium between them (see CAMBIUM; DICOTYLEDON). The cambium produces new xylem and phloem and causes the stem to increase in width. As the stems get older, the bundles gradually join to form a solid ring.

In monocotyledonous plants, the xylem and phloem are mixed in bundles scattered throughout the stem (see MONOCOTYLEDON). These bundles do not have cambium, and the stems therefore do not increase in width.

**Types of stems** There are two basic types of stems: herbaceous and woody (see HERBACEOUS PLANT; WOODY PLANT). Herbaceous stems are relatively weak. Most of their strength comes from turgor pressure, which is the pressure of liquid within their cells (see OSMOSIS). Many herbaceous stems are green and are capable of a certain amount of photosynthesis (see PHOTOSYNTHESIS). Most annual plants have herbaceous stems. The stems of biennial and perennial herbaceous plants usually die in the winter, and new ones grow in the spring (see ANNUAL PLANT; BIENNIAL PLANT; PERENNIAL PLANT).

Woody stems are much stronger than herbaceous stems. They have special fibers and tracheids (cells), which add strength and rigidity. Most woody stems are green when they are young. As they grow older, however, they lose their green color and no longer are capable of photosynthesis.

Some stems are thick and fleshy, storing water or food for future use. Some stems grow horizontally underground and are called rhizomes (see RHIZOME). Some underground stems become thickened with stored food (see BULB AND CORM; TUBER). Some stems grow horizontally, just above the surface of the ground. These stems are called stolons or runners. They give rise to new plants at several places along their length. Some stems produce protective structures to keep animals from eating them (see THORN, SPINE, AND PRICKLE). In some plants, such as the cacti, the stems take over completely the food-producing work of the leaves.

*See also* ANNUAL RING.

**STENTOR** (stĕn′tôr′) A stentor is a microscopic protozoan found in fresh water (see PROTOZOA). It consists of a single cell that can be as much as 0.1 in. [2.5 mm] long, which is large for a protozoan. The stentor is trumpet shaped when attached to a surface. However, when it swims, it has a round shape. The stentor feeds by sweeping in smaller organisms with a ring of fused (joined) cilia located around the large end of the trumpet (see CILIUM).

**STEREOSCOPE** (stĕr′ē ə skōp′) The ability to see things in depth is called stereoscopic vision. When we look at an object, particularly a nearby object, our eyes tell us more or less how far away it is and what sort of shape it has. Because we have two eyes, we are able to see things in three dimensions, or in depth. Each eye sees an object slightly differently, because it picks up light from the object from a slightly different angle. This allows us to view things in three dimensions.

A stereoscope is a device to reproduce the three-dimensional effect from a flat surface. It consists of

Terminal bud
Lateral bud
Internode
Node
Terminal bud

**STEM**

The horse chestnut stem at left shows the typical features of a plant stem.

a box or framework with a lens for each eye (see LENS). Two photographs of an object or scene, taken from slightly different positions, are viewed through the stereoscope. One eye sees one photograph, and the other eye sees the other photograph. The images are brought together by the eyes to form a single view, which gives the impression of depth. Elaborate forms of stereoscopes are used to prepare maps from photographs taken by aircraft or satellites.

*See also* EYE AND VISION; MAP AND MAPPING.

**STEREOSCOPE**

Stereoscopes were popular in the 1800s. They were designed so that each eye looked at a slightly different view of a scene, giving a three-dimensional effect.

**STERILIZATION** (stĕr′ə lĭ zā′shən) Sterilization is the killing of microorganisms to prevent infection and the spread of disease (see DISEASE; INFECTION; MICROORGANISM). The bandages and medicines that we buy are sterilized. Doctors and dentists sterilize their instruments before using them on the human body.

Most sterilization is done by steam, hot air, fire, or certain chemicals. Steam and hot air are the most widely used methods of sterilizing objects because they do not leave foreign matter on the sterilized objects. Doctors and dentists sterilize their instruments in steam cabinets.

Pasteurization is the partial sterilizing of food, such as milk and cheese, so that it can stay fresh for days or weeks. This is accomplished by heating and then quickly cooling the food (see PASTEURIZATION).

Sterilization also means rendering a man or woman, or another male or female animal, infertile. A man or woman can have an operation that ensures that thereafter he or she will not have any children.

*See also* CONTRACEPTION.

**STERNUM** (stûr′nəm) The sternum, or breastbone, is a large, flat bone in the center of the human chest. Seven pairs of ribs are attached to the sternum by cartilage. The sternum and the ribs protect many of the body's vital organs.

*See also* CARTILAGE; RIB; SKELETON.

**STEROID** (stîr′oid′) Steroids are a group of organic (carbon-containing) compounds produced by plants and animals. Steroids can also be made artificially. Steroids are similar in structure, but each compound has a unique biological function (see COMPOUND).

All steroid molecules have a basic structure in which carbon atoms, which are arranged in rings, are attached to hydrogen atoms (see ATOM; MOLECULE). Variations in this structure determine the biological function of the particular steroid.

One group of steroids are the sterols. Cholesterol is an example of a sterol (see CHOLESTEROL). Cholesterol is found in the blood, tissues, and organs of the human body. Cholesterol is used by the body to produce the sex hormones (see HORMONE). The sex hormones are also steroids. Testosterone, estrogen, and progesterone are examples of sex hormones.

Hormones produced by the adrenal glands, such as cortisone and related compounds, are also steroids (see ADRENAL GLANDS). These compounds help the body adjust to changes in the environment and reduce inflammation in cases of injury or infection (see INFECTION; INFLAMMATION). Other steroids that the body releases perform varied tasks. For example, they aid digestion, control the absorption of sodium and potassium, and stimulate muscle development.

Humans receive some steroids when they eat

certain animal foods. Cholesterol is one example. Another example is vitamin D, a steroid that is found in fish and dairy products. Vitamin D is important in maintaining strong bones (see VITAMIN). Humans can also take in artificial steroids. Artificial steroids are sometimes used by athletes who want to improve their performance. Many scientists believe that this practice can be damaging to the athlete's body. The exact effects on the body are a source of controversy, however. The use of steroids is prohibited by the organizations that regulate amateur athletics.

## STETHOSCOPE (stĕth′ə skōp′) A stethoscope is a device used by physicians to listen to sounds inside a patient's body. The sounds made by the rushing of blood through the heart valves and the closing of the valves can give valuable clues to different heart diseases. The sounds made by air in the bronchioles in the lungs may help indicate disorders of the lung tissue (see HEART; LUNG). A stethoscope may also be used to listen to the sounds made by the heart of an unborn baby. A stethoscope consists basically of a contact piece, which may be a bell shape or a thin diaphragm (disk) that conducts sound through rubber or plastic tubing to a pair of earpieces, which fit into the physician's ears.

PROJECT 64

**STETHOSCOPE**

A physician uses a stethoscope to listen for sounds in a patient's heart and lungs.

## STEVENS, NETTIE (1861–1912) Nettie Stevens was an American biologist who discovered that the sex of an organism is determined by the presence of a certain combination of chromosomes (see CHROMOSOME; SEX). Stevens was born in 1861 in Vermont. She received degrees from Stanford University in California and from Bryn Mawr College in Pennsylvania. She taught biology and did research on how the sex of insects and plants is determined. Stevens also became interested in how the sex of humans is determined.

In 1906, Stevens found that the human female sex cell (ovum or egg) has a kind of chromosome that she named the X chromosome and twenty-two other chromosomes (see X CHROMOSOME). The male sex cell (sperm), however, could have either an X chromosome or another kind of chromosome that Stevens named the Y chromosome, along with twenty-two other chromosomes (see Y CHROMOSOME). When the sperm fertilizes the egg, their chromosomes combine into pairs (see FERTILIZATION). Stevens discovered that if a sperm with an X chromosome fertilized an egg, the two X chromosomes would combine, and a female would result. If a sperm with a Y chromosome fertilized an egg, the Y and X chromosomes would combine, and a male would result. Stevens' discovery was not

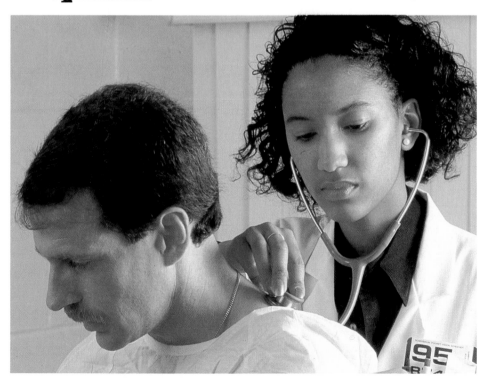

universally accepted at the time she announced her findings. However, today her findings are recognized as a valid explanation of how the sex of an organism is determined.

**STICKLEBACK** A stickleback is a small fish that belongs to the family Gasterosteidae. It is called a stickleback because it has a number of small spines on its back, in front of a soft dorsal (back) fin. These spines are used to protect the fish from larger fish that may try to eat it.

There are several species of sticklebacks in North American waters. They are found in fresh water and shallow coastal salt water. Most species average from 2 to 2.5 in. [5 to 6.4 cm] in length.

In sticklebacks, the male instead of the female fish cares for the young. He constructs a nest with pieces of water plants and twigs, glued together with a threadlike material from his body. The nest—a small, barrel-shaped structure—is usually built among the stems of water plants. The female stickleback lays eggs inside the nest and then leaves. The male fish protects the eggs and young fish until they are able to protect themselves.
*See also* FISH.

**STIGMA** (stĭg′mə) The stigma is that part of the pistil, or female sex organ of a flower, that receives the pollen (see POLLEN; POLLINATION). It is located at the top of the pistil (see PISTIL). Its sticky or feathery surface catches and holds any pollen grains that fall on it. After landing on the stigma, the pollen grows a pollen tube into it. Eventually, this pollen tube pushes its way down the style, the

**STIGMA**

This tulip flower has been cut open to reveal the female pistil (the white structure) with a lobed stigma at the end. The dark structures are male anthers covered in pollen.

slender tubelike part of the pistil. At the bottom, it reaches the ovary and attaches to an ovule. Inside the ovule, a sperm nucleus from the pollen grain fuses with an egg, and the egg is fertilized (see FERTILIZATION). The fertilized egg develops into an embryo (see EMBRYO). The ovule develops into a seed, and the ovary becomes a fruit. The stigma contains chemicals that prevent the wrong types of pollen from growing on it.
*See also* FLOWER; REPRODUCTION.

**STIMULANT** (stĭm′yə lənt) A stimulant is a drug that increases the activity of all or part of the body. Stimulants, such as amphetamines, caffeine (found in tea, coffee, cocoa, and some soft drinks), and nicotine (found in tobacco), may make a person feel more alert and energetic (see AMPHETAMINE; CAFFEINE). They do so by stimulating the central nervous system (see NERVOUS SYSTEM).

Different doses of stimulants have different effects on the body. For example, a small dose of the stimulant strychnine makes a drowsy person more wakeful. A large dose of this drug, however, may cause great harm and sometimes death. Also, a person who takes a stimulant such as an amphetamine may later undergo a period of depression as an aftereffect. Stimulants are sometimes prescribed by doctors to treat certain sleep disorders, to help people lose weight, or for other purposes. Such stimulants can be dangerous if used incorrectly and should only be used under a doctor's supervision.
*See also* DRUG.

**STIMULUS** (stĭm′yə ləs) A stimulus is something in the outside world that may cause an organism to respond or change its behavior. For example, light is a stimulus to most flowers. It causes the petals to open. Darkness, another stimulus, causes the petals to close. In humans and other higher animals, a stimulus is usually considered to be anything that triggers an impulse from a kind of nerve cell called a receptor (see NERVE CELL; RECEPTOR; SENSE). For example, a receptor in your finger would be stimulated if a sharp pin touched your fingertip. Your nerves would carry the message to your central nervous system (see NERVOUS SYSTEM).

If a stimulus results in an automatic response, the sequence is known as a reflex action (see REFLEX). One example of a reflex action is when you automatically pull your hand away from a hot object.

**STOMA** (stō'mə) A stoma is a tiny opening in the epidermis of a leaf. It allows air and water vapor to move in and out of a leaf. In most leaves, the majority of stomata (plural of *stoma*) are on the underside of the leaf. In some leaves, however, the stomata are fairly evenly divided between the upper and lower surfaces.

The stomata are usually open during the day. Thus, air can move in and out of the leaf through the stomata. The air entering contains carbon dioxide, which is absorbed by many cells in the leaf and is used in photosynthesis (see PHOTOSYNTHESIS). Air also moves out of the leaf. The air leaving the leaf contains more oxygen and less carbon dioxide than the air entering the leaf. Oxygen is a waste product of photosynthesis. Also, the air moving out of a leaf contains water vapor. This loss of water vapor is called transpiration (see TRANSPIRATION). During the night in the absence of light, photosynthesis stops and carbon dioxide is not needed. The stomata close at night. This helps the leaf save water by decreasing the amount of water vapor lost through transpiration.

Each stoma is surrounded by a pair of guard cells.

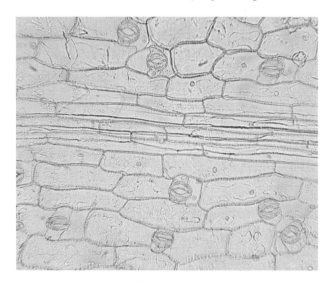

**STOMA**

In this microscope photograph of the underside of a leaf, the stomata (plural of *stoma*) are the small oval structures. They are open to allow carbon dioxide to enter the leaf.

Each guard cell is a specialized epidermal cell. The action of the guard cells is controlled by their turgor pressure, or the amount of water within these cells (see OSMOSIS). When the guard cells are swollen with water, the stoma is open. When the cells contain less water, the stoma is closed. *See also* LEAF.

**STOMACH** (stŭm'ək) The stomach is an important organ of digestion in many animals (see DIGESTIVE SYSTEM). It is part of the alimentary canal (see ALIMENTARY CANAL). Located between the esophagus and the small intestine, the stomach is a muscular, baglike organ (see ESOPHAGUS; INTESTINE). In a group of mammals called ruminants, the stomach has three or four chambers (see RUMINANT). In most other animals, the stomach has a single chamber.

In humans, the stomach has two main functions: storage and digestion. The adult stomach can hold about 1.06 quarts [1 liter]. The stomach produces gastric juices made up of hydrochloric acid, a slippery fluid called mucus, and enzymes. The hydrochloric acid activates an enzyme and kills most microorganisms in the food (see MICROORGANISMS). The mucus helps protect the stomach lining and lubricates the food. The enzymes pepsin and rennin begin digesting the proteins in the food (see ENZYME). The stomach mixes the food and the gastric juices by churning them together. This produces a semiliquid mass called chyme. The chyme normally stays in the stomach for three to five hours. Then it is pushed from the stomach into the small intestine by waves of muscle contractions called peristalsis (see PERISTALSIS).

The stomach is usually conditioned, or trained, to "expect" food at certain times every day. At these times, peristalsis begins, and gastric juices are released. These produce hunger pangs and, at times, a "growling" stomach.

Sometimes, the stomach produces more than the usual amount of gastric juices. If these juices back up into the esophagus, they cause an unpleasant sensation called heartburn. Larger amounts of gastric juices are released in times of emotional stress and can irritate the stomach lining. The stomach lining also can be irritated by very spicy foods. Smoking cigarettes or drinking beverages containing alcohol or caffeine also can irritate the stomach. The combination of an irritated stomach lining and too much gastric juice may be factors leading to the formation of a peptic ulcer. A peptic ulcer is an open sore in the lining of the stomach or small intestine. It is often very painful. It may perforate, or break through, the entire stomach or intestinal wall and release substances into the abdominal cavity. A person with an ulcer should be treated by a doctor. Medical treatment and controlling the diet can help heal ulcers.

## STONE AGE

The Stone Age is the period of time when people made and used stone tools. It ended when people learned how to shape metal into tools.

The Stone Age is divided into three periods: the Paleolithic, or Old Stone Age; the Mesolithic, or Middle Stone Age; and the Neolithic, or New Stone Age. In Europe, the Paleolithic includes all of humanity's prehistory until about ten thousand years ago. Paleolithic people were all hunters and gatherers. Their tools were generally crude. During the Mesolithic, much finer stone tools were made. The Mesolithic saw the first use of the bow and arrow for hunting. During the Neolithic, farming and the manufacture of pottery became widespread

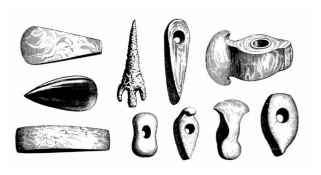

**STONE AGE**
A selection of tools used during the Stone Age is shown above. Some of the tools were held in the hand. Others were used as spear or ax heads.

in Europe. Neolithic people learned how to grind and polish stone to make tools and weapons. Most Native Americans were living a Neolithic life-style when Europeans first arrived in the Americas. *See also* PREHISTORY.

## STONECROP FAMILY

The stonecrop, or orpine, family includes 1,500 species of perennial herbaceous plants and shrubs (see HERBACEOUS PLANT; PERENNIAL PLANT; SHRUB). Most are native to dry, rocky areas. They have thick, fleshy leaves, and many form carpets or rosettes on the ground. The five-petal, starlike flowers grow in clusters. They may be red, white, or yellow. As well as the stonecrops, the family includes the houseleeks and kalanchoes, which are both popular houseplants.

**STONECROP FAMILY**
The stonecrop, so called because it often grows on old walls, has clusters of white, yellow, or red flowers.

**STONE FLY** Stone flies are insects that belong to the order Plecoptera (see INSECT). Because they have four wings (not two), they are not true flies. The adults range in length from 0.2 to 2.0 in. [0.4 to 5 cm]. Their bodies are usually dull brown or green, allowing the insects to blend in with the area around them (see CAMOUFLAGE). The adults live for only a few days. They die soon after they mate and lay eggs.

The eggs hatch into nymphs (see NYMPH). The nymphs live beneath stones and other objects in clear streams and ponds. They eat tiny plant and animal matter. Nymphs molt (lose their outer covering) thirty to forty times before becoming adults (see MOLTING). The nymphs are a favorite food of trout and other freshwater fish.

**STORK**

Storks are noted for their long legs and necks. Pictured here are the black stork (left) and the whale-headed stork.

**STORK** A stork is a tall bird that belongs to the family Ciconiidae. It has a long, thin neck, bill, and legs. A stork eats small water animals such as frogs, fish, and insects, which it spears with its bill. A stork often wades through marshy areas to catch its food.

There are several species of storks found in the world. The best known is the European white stork, which spends the summer in Europe and the winter in southern Africa. It often nests on rooftops in Europe, where it is believed to be a sign of good luck. The only true stork native to the United States is the wood stork, often called wood ibis by mistake. The wood stork has a white body and a black head. Although most wood storks live in Florida, some live in the other southern states.

**STORM** A storm is a disturbance in the atmosphere that causes wind and rain, snow, or other precipitation (see ATMOSPHERE; PRECIPITATION; WIND). Storms are sometimes divided into two groups: small-scale storms and large-scale storms.

Small-scale storms include thunderstorms and tornadoes. These storms usually affect only a small area. Thunderstorms cause lightning, thunder, rain

**STORM—Thunderstorms**
Violent thunderstorms, such as the one approaching the community in the picture, can develop quickly. Their winds, precipitation, and lightning cause a great deal of damage worldwide.

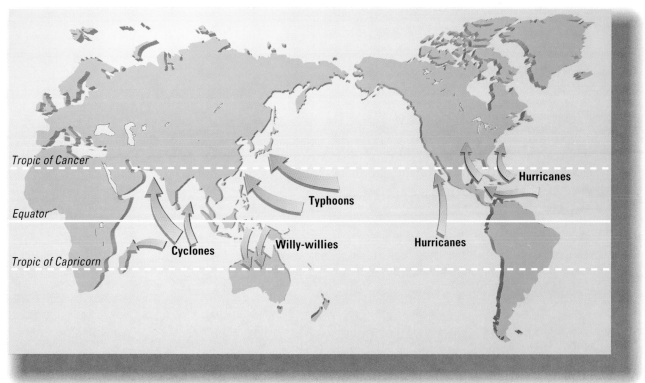

**STORM—Tropical storm activity**

Areas of tropical storm activity in different parts of the world are shown above. The same kind of tropical storm has different names depending on where it occurs.

and sometimes hail, and strong, gusty winds. A tornado often develops under conditions that cause large thunderstorms. Tornadoes cause the strongest winds found on the earth's surface (see THUNDERSTORM; TORNADO).

A large-scale storm affects a large area. Some large-scale storms are found in the tropics, near the equator, while others happen in temperate regions. In the Northern Hemisphere, wind in large-scale storms moves in a counterclockwise (opposite to a clock's hand) direction around an area of low air pressure (see DEPRESSION). In the Southern Hemisphere, the wind moves in a clockwise direction. In both cases, the movement is called cyclonic (see CYCLONE). A very strong tropical cyclone may be a hurricane or a typhoon (see HURRICANE). In temperate regions, cyclones occur along warm or cold fronts (see FRONT). Such cyclones try to mix the air behind the cold front with the air behind the warm front. These storms often bring heavy rain or snow and strong winds.

**STRATIFICATION** (străt'ə f ĭ kā'shən) Stratification is the arrangement of rocks in horizontal layers. These layers are called strata. The strata may be from a few inches to several feet thick. Most sedimentary rock is stratified (see ROCK; SEDIMENTARY ROCK).

**STRATIFICATION**

Stratification is the arrangement of rocks in layers called strata. These are clearly shown in this view of a steep-sided, dried-up river valley.

Stratification occurs when different kinds of matter, called sediment, are laid down by the action of water on land or under a lake or ocean. More matter covers each layer. After a long time, the pressure, or weight, from above causes the layers below to harden into rock.

Stratification is found in igneous rock as well as in sedimentary rock (see IGNEOUS ROCK). Lava and ash from volcanoes form layers that harden as they cool (see VOLCANO). These layers make up a type of stratified rock.

Stratified rocks help scientists date fossils and determine when certain geological events occurred (see DATING; FOSSIL). The lower strata of these rocks are generally older than the upper strata.

**STRATOSPHERE** (străt′ə sfîr′) The stratosphere is the level of the atmosphere above the troposphere (see ATMOSPHERE; TROPOSPHERE AND TROPOPAUSE). It begins at a height of 5 to 10 mi. [8 to 16 km] above the ground—a boundary known as the tropopause—and reaches up to about 50 mi. [80 km]. At the top of the stratosphere is a boundary called the stratopause, and beyond that are the ionosphere and exosphere (see IONOSPHERE). The stratosphere contains about 19 percent of the earth's atmosphere by weight, but only about 5.5 percent of the atmosphere by volume. It contains the ozone layer, the barrier that prevents the sun's dangerous ultraviolet rays from reaching the ground (see OZONE LAYER; ULTRAVIOLET RAY). The air in the stratosphere is too thin to be warmed much by the sun's rays, so there are no convection currents and few clouds (see CLOUD; CONVECTION). The stratosphere may contain dust particles that have been blasted into the atmosphere by volcanic eruptions. Large amounts of such dust could affect global climate. High-speed aircraft fly in the stratosphere.

**STRAWBERRY** Strawberries are plants belonging to genus *Fragaria* of the rose family, Rosaceae (see ROSE FAMILY). Strawberry plants grow close to the ground. They have compound leaves with three hairy leaflets, with toothed margins (see LEAF). Clusters of white flowers grow in the leaf axils, between the leaf and the stem. Special stems called

**STRAWBERRY**

Strawberry plants (top) have five-petaled flowers that resemble small wild roses. The pips or "seeds" on the outside of the strawberry (bottom) are actually tiny fruits.

runners grow horizontally along the ground surface and root at their tips. New plants sprout from the rooted parts of these runners (see STEM; VEGETATIVE PROPAGATION).

The plant produces a fruit called a strawberry. However, this fruit is not a true berry. It is an enlarged receptacle (see BERRY; RECEPTACLE). The many "seeds" on the outside of a strawberry are really tiny fruits on the receptacle. Strawberries are tasty and sweet. They are among the most popular of the small fruits grown in warm areas of the Northern Hemisphere, and many varieties are now cultivated. Strawberries are rich in vitamin C, iron, and other minerals. They can be eaten alone or used in desserts.

*See also* FRUIT; VITAMIN.

**STREAMLINING** Streamlining is the process of designing a moving body so that it moves efficiently through water or air. Streamlining is important for designing aircraft and ships. When aircraft or ships move, the air or water tends to resist, or hold back, their movement. This effect is called drag (see DRAG). Drag prevents the aircraft or ship from traveling as fast as it might.

With bodies moving slower than the speed of sound, the pressure of the air or water increases at the front of the body and is less at the rear. If the surface shape of the body is not smooth, the air or water flowing past the surface becomes turbulent, or rough. This adds to the drag. To reduce the drag, a streamlined body has a teardrop shape with a smooth surface. The front is rounded and the rear is pointed.

At speeds faster than that of sound, a different effect, called wave drag, appears. Waves of compressed air occur at both the front and the tail of the moving body. Along the middle of the moving body, an expansion wave occurs. These waves produce drag and a loud noise called a sonic boom. To reduce this type of drag, the moving body needs a pointed nose and a pointed tail.

*See also* AERODYNAMICS; AERONAUTICS; WAVE.

**STRENGTH OF MATERIAL** A number of different materials are used for building and other purposes. These materials have to hold up under various forces and loads that could break or bend them. For instance, engine parts have to hold up under constant vibrations. Wire has to keep its form under great tension. For these reasons, it is important to know the strengths of different materials.

The forces that materials must withstand are often complicated. They are divided into different types. Scientists and engineers are usually most concerned with a type of force called a stress. Stresses tend to change the shape or size of a body. This change is called strain (see STRESS AND STRAIN). One kind of stress is called tensile stress. It is a stress that stretches a body. Brittle materials, such as glass, stretch only a little and break easily. Metals, however, stretch more before they break. If the stress is not too great, most metals return to their original shape when the stress is removed. They are said to be elastic (see ELASTICITY). Above a certain stress, the material will not return to its original shape. This stress is called the elastic limit. At a certain higher stress, the material breaks. This stress is called the ultimate tensile strength.

Wires and threads are tested by stretching them until they break. Bars and rods are often tested by bending them. The tensile strength can be determined from the load needed to break the rod and from other factors.

Another form of stress is called shear stress. A shear stress occurs when a sliding force is applied to a body. For example, a shear stress on two metal plates bolted together may break the bolts.

Still another form of stress is compression. This type of stress squashes a body. A body may be compressed from all directions. This is the force that bodies experience deep in the sea. The compression can also take place in just one direction. This stress occurs when a person sits on something. Brittle materials are much stronger under compression

**STRENGTH OF MATERIAL**

A helicopter is made of materials that are chosen for their strength and lightness. They include the plastic canopy (cockpit cover), aluminum fuselage (body of helicopter), and carbon-fiber rotor.

than they are when stretched. Metals, on the other hand, are weaker under compression than they are when stretched.

The final important kind of stress is torsion. Torsion is a twisting stress. It occurs, for example, in objects that turn (see TORSION). Under torsion, brittle materials start to form tiny cracks on the surface.

Some composite materials, such as carbon fiber and boron fiber, are extremely strong and can resist high temperatures.

**STREP THROAT** Strep throat is an infectious disease, usually occurring in epidemics. It is caused by the toxins (poisons) released by members of a group of bacteria called group A *Streptococcus* (see BACTERIA; DISEASE; INFECTION; TOXIN).

Symptoms of strep throat include a red and swollen throat, fever, and headache. Sometimes, chills and vomiting occur. Symptoms develop within three days of exposure to the bacteria. Treatment is often with penicillin (see PENICILLIN). Penicillin works by making it difficult for bacteria to multiply. Most patients treated with penicillin or other antibiotics recover from strep throat quickly (see ANTIBIOTIC). Untreated patients usually recover after about two weeks. Timely treatment is important because strep throat can lead to more serious illnesses, such as rheumatic fever (see RHEUMATIC FEVER). A vaccination has not yet been developed against strep throat. To avoid the spread of the bacteria that cause strep throat, a person should limit contact with others who may have the disease.
*See also* VACCINATION.

**STRESS AND STRAIN** If a force is applied to an object, it may cause the object to change shape or size. For example, a force easily changes the shape of a piece of rubber. Stress is the force acting on a body, divided by an area. Strain is a measure of the change in the shape of a body under stress.

The most common kind of stress is a stretching force. This is called tensile stress, or tension. In this case, the stress is the force divided by the area of the cross section of the body. The strain is the increase in length divided by the original length. For most materials, the strain is proportional to the stress. This means that twice the stress strains the body by twice the amount. The body is then said to be elastic (see ELASTICITY). This relationship is called Hooke's law.

There are two other main kinds of stress and strain. One stress is compressive stress, or compression, which squashes a body. It produces a strain called a volume strain because the volume of the body decreases. The volume strain is the change in volume divided by the original volume (see VOLUME).

The other main kind of stress is called a shear stress. This is a stress that acts along one face of a body. For example, imagine that your hand is resting on a book that is flat on a table. If you push your hand along the top of the book, you are causing a shear stress on the book. A shear stress changes the shape of an object but does not change its volume. The shear stress produces a shear strain. The shear strain measures the amount by which a body changes its shape.

Knowledge of stress and strain for various materials is very important in engineering. An engineer has to know how a structure will behave under certain stresses.
*See also* STRENGTH OF MATERIAL.

Unstressed

Tension

Compression

Shear

**STRESS AND STRAIN**

The diagrams show how various stresses—tension, compression, and shear—can change the shape of a block.

**STRESS, HUMAN** Human stress is a reaction by the body to demanding stimuli (plural of *stimulus*) (see STIMULUS). These stimuli may be pleasant, such as a hug, or unpleasant, such as a kick. Both kinds of stimuli cause certain predictable reactions in the body. For example, during stress, muscles tense, and heart rate and blood pressure increase. The body also has increased energy levels. This article will concentrate on stress caused by unpleasant stimuli. Such stress can have significant long-term negative effects on the body.

The stimulus that causes stress is called a stressor. There are different kinds of stressors. Biological stressors include disease and physical exhaustion. Environmental stressors include noise, overcrowding, and natural disasters, such as earthquakes. Behavioral stressors include eating a diet that is nutritionally poor, smoking, and abusing alcohol or certain other drugs (see DRUG; NUTRITION; SMOKING). Sometimes, a person's life situation can be a stressor. For example, difficulties at home, school, or work may cause stress. Mental challenges, such as tests or contests, are also stressors.

The body may pass through stages during stress. The first stage is called alarm. During this stage, the adrenal glands release certain hormones that help provide an immediate increase in energy and suppress the workings of the body's immune system (see ADRENAL GLANDS; HORMONE; IMMUNITY). The adrenal glands also release other hormones that increase the blood pressure and heart rate. In addition, the muscles tense.

Prolonged stress, or the occurrence of many stressors at one time, may cause the body to enter the second and perhaps the third stages of stress. The second stage of stress is called resistance. In resistance, the person may have a strong resistance to one kind of stressor, but a low resistance to another. For example, the person may be able to perform well in a contest but is more likely to get certain diseases, such as the common cold. The third stage of stress is called exhaustion. In exhaustion, resistance to all stressors is low. A person has a greatly increased chance of contracting certain diseases. Some diseases associated with prolonged stress include abnormal heart rhythms, colitis (inflammation of the intestine), chronic fatigue syndrome, mononucleosis, herpes simplex, ulcers (sores in the lining of the intestine), and even certain cancers. Mental depression and the inability to think clearly or concentrate may occur (see CANCER; DEPRESSION (MENTAL); HEART DISEASE; HERPES; INTESTINE; MONONUCLEOSIS).

Research has shown that stress can be reduced or eliminated by following certain actions. These include exercising regularly, eating a proper diet, and getting enough rest (see DIET). Some people can use biofeedback to control their reactions to stress (see BIOFEEDBACK). Avoiding smoking or the abuse of alcohol or other nonmedical drugs also can help prevent stress. Stress research was pioneered by Canadian scientist Hans Selye in the late 1930s.

**STROBOSCOPE** (strō′bə skōp′) A stroboscope is an instrument that measures the rate at which objects rotate (spin) or vibrate (move back and forth). It is also used to study objects while they are

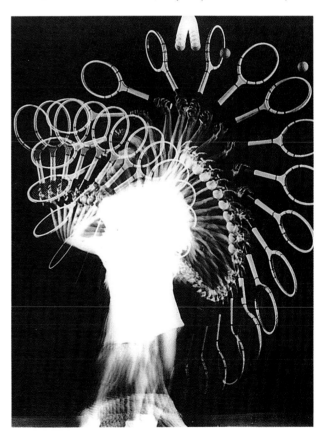

**STROBOSCOPE**
This multiple-exposure photograph of a tennis player was taken with the aid of a stroboscope.

moving. A stroboscope gives out bright flashes of light. The time between the flashes can be changed. A dial on the stroboscope shows how fast the light is flashing.

To measure the rate at which an object is rotating or vibrating, the stroboscope is shone onto the object. The rate of the stroboscope's flashing is then adjusted until the object appears to stop moving. This occurs when the rate of flashing of the strobo-scope is equal to the rate at which the object is rotating or vibrating.

Stroboscopes are used by garage mechanics to observe rotating automobile wheels. In laboratories, stroboscopes are sometimes used to observe vibrating strings and springs. Photographs can be taken by light from a stroboscope. This is a valuable way of studying a fast-moving object, such as a swinging golf club, tennis racket, or baseball bat. **PROJECT 55**

**STROKE** Stroke is a condition that results when the brain does not receive the proper amount of blood. This can result in brain damage and even death.

A stroke may be caused by a blood clot, called a thrombus, that forms in an artery in the brain or in an artery leading to the brain. However, some clots may form elsewhere in the body, such as the heart. The clot may then travel through the body's large blood vessels until it gets stuck in one of the brain's small blood vessels. Often, the clot forms at a point of arteriosclerosis (see ARTERIOSCLEROSIS; ARTERY). Sometimes, a stroke is caused by a broken blood vessel in the brain.

During a stroke, the brain does not receive enough blood, so it does not receive the proper amount of oxygen and nutrients. Without the proper amount of oxygen and nutrients, the brain may be permanently injured. Because the brain controls the entire body, the regions of the body controlled by the injured part of the brain will be affected. Victims of stroke may suffer paralysis. They may be unable to walk or talk.

A stroke may be prevented by removing blood clots through surgery, by the use of certain drugs, or by the surgical repair of broken blood vessels. *See also* CIRCULATORY SYSTEM.

**STURGEON** (stûr´jən) A sturgeon is a fish that belongs to the family Acipenseridae. It is an ancient fish with a skeleton made up mostly of cartilage instead of bone, although its body is covered with large bony plates (see BONE; CARTILAGE; SKELETON).

A sturgeon sucks up worms, insects, and other small animals off the bottom of a river, lake, or ocean. Several species of sturgeon live in North American waters. Some live only in fresh water, but others live in the oceans and swim up freshwater rivers to spawn (see SPAWNING).

Sturgeons are among the largest freshwater fish in the world. The white sturgeon often weighs several hundred pounds. One sturgeon was reported to weigh over 1,800 lb. [810 kg]. Sturgeons may live for over a hundred years. Sturgeon eggs, called caviar, are considered a delicacy by some people. *See also* FISH.

**STURGEON**
The sturgeon (above) is an ancient fish that is covered with large bony plates.

**SUBLIMATION** (sŭb´lə mā´ shən) When most solids are heated, they eventually melt and become liquid. Then, at a higher temperature, the liquid boils to form a gas. However, a few substances go directly from their solid state to a gaseous state. This is called sublimation. The reverse happens when a gas turns directly into a solid. This is also called sublimation. Iodine and carbon dioxide are examples of substances that sublime. Because solid carbon dioxide does not liquefy (turn into liquid) when heated at normal pressures, it is known as dry ice. It turns from a solid directly into a gas (see CARBON DIOXIDE). Substances that sublime can be made to liquefy. This is done by heating them under pressure. *See also* STATES OF MATTER.

A submarine is a ship that operates under water. The submarine is mainly a weapon of war. It was used in World Wars I and II (1914–1918 and 1939–1945). Today, nuclear-powered missile-carrying submarines are important to the United States defense system.

Some submarines are built for peaceful uses. Small submarines that can carry from one to six persons are used to hunt for sunken treasure and for research in the oceans (see OCEANOGRAPHY).

**What submarines are like** Most submarines are shaped like a cigar, with tapered ends and an almost round body. They have flipperlike control surfaces, called diving planes, mounted at the front end, and rudders, additional diving planes, and propellers at the rear end. The diving planes control the ship's up-and-down movements. A tall structure, called a conning tower, rises above the top of the submarine just forward of the midpoint. The conning tower contains the control and navigation center. The bridge, or top deck of the conning tower, is used for navigating when the submarine is on the surface. The conning tower also contains the periscope, a kind of telescope that is used for observing the surface when the ship is submerged (see PERISCOPE). The conning tower of today's submarines is called the sail. It is highly streamlined to reduce drag, which is the force of the water tending to hold the ship back (see DRAG; STREAMLINING).

Submarines have two steel hulls, or frames—an inner hull and an outer hull. Submarines need these two hulls for protection against the pressure of water, which reaches 88 lb. per sq. in. [6.2 kg per sq. cm] of hull surface at a depth of 200 ft. [62 m]. The space between the hulls is filled with water. This reduces the pressure on the outside hull.

Until the development of nuclear power plants in the 1950s, submarines used diesel or gasoline engines on the surface and electric motors under water (see ELECTRIC MOTOR; ENGINE). Electric motors were used under water because they did not need air to operate. Large rows of batteries were used to supply power to these motors (see BATTERY). Consequently, a submarine had to spend long hours on the surface recharging these batteries. During World War II, the Germans developed a device called a snorkel. The snorkel is a long breathing tube connected to a small float on the surface. The snorkel supplies a continuous flow of air to the diesel engine so that it can operate under water. Most of the submarines used in World War II could travel at about 20 knots (22 m.p.h. or 35 kph) on the surface, and about 10 knots (11 m.p.h. or 18 kph) under water.

The nuclear power plants used in most modern submarines do not need air to operate. These ships can stay underwater for months at a time without refueling. They also are much faster—both on the surface and underwater—than older submarines (see NUCLEAR ENERGY).

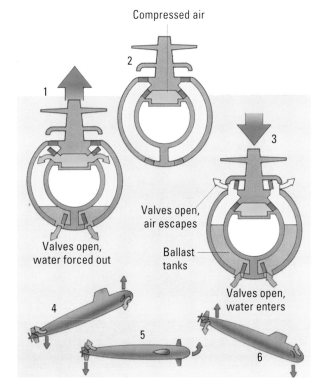

Compressed air

Valves open, air escapes

Valves open, water forced out

Ballast tanks

Valves open, water enters

**DIVING AND STEERING**

The ballast tanks in a submerged submarine are full of water. (1) To surface, compressed air forces the water out of the tanks. (2) On the surface, the tanks are empty. (3) To submerge, the tanks are flooded. The nose of the submarine rises or falls by moving the diving planes (4) up, or (6) down. (5) Sideways control is achieved by moving the rudder.

**GERMAN U-BOAT**

German submarines known as U-boats (for "undersea boat") came close to winning the Battle of the Atlantic against the Allies in World War II. The Type VII submarine shown below had five torpedo tubes—four in front and one in the rear. It carried fourteen torpedoes, which it used to sink Allied ships.

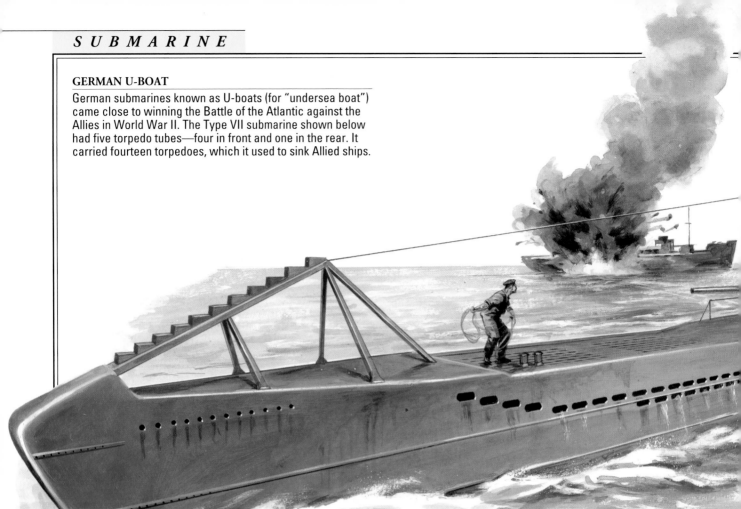

Most World War II submarines were about 330 ft. [100 m] in length and 16 ft. [5 m] in width. Many of today's submarines are about that size, though some of the missile-carrying kinds are much larger. The older submarines had tubes in the bow and stem (front and rear) from which to fire torpedoes, a kind of missile that contains explosives and travels underwater under its own power.

Modern submarines employed for defense are usually divided into two kinds: ballistic missile submarines and attack submarines. Missile submarines are the larger of the two. They carry a number of large intercontinental ballistic missiles that can be fired from underwater locations. These huge missiles can destroy enemy targets thousands of miles away (see MISSILE).

Attack submarines are smaller and faster than missile submarines. They are armed with torpedoes and other weapons. They can attack enemy submarines and surface ships in the event of war. The United States and Russia have the largest fleets of both kinds of submarines in the world.

A submarine operates on the surface just like any other ship. When it goes under water, water is allowed to enter and fill tanks called ballast tanks. This makes the submarine heavier than water, and it sinks below the surface. The diving planes, which are controlled from inside the submarine, control the angle of descent. When the submarine has reached its desired depth, some of the water is forced out of the ballast tanks, and the submarine levels off. Most military submarines can dive to a

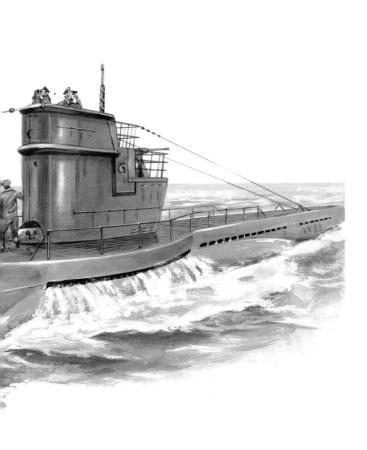

depth of over 98 ft. [30 m] in less than a minute.

Once under water, some submarines change to electric motors for forward movement. Nuclear submarines continue to use their normal engines. To get back to the surface, submarines blow water out of the ballast tanks with compressed air. This makes the ship rise toward the surface. Again, the diving planes control the angle of ascent.

**History** David Bushnell, an American inventor, built the first submarine during the American Revolution. It was named the *Turtle.* The *Turtle* made an unsuccessful attack on a British ship in New York Harbor. In 1800, Robert Fulton, the inventor of the steamboat, built a copper-coated submarine that saw limited use (see FULTON, ROBERT). In 1898, John P. Holland designed and constructed the United States Navy's first submarine. It was 53 ft. [16 m] long and displaced 75 tons [67.5 metric tons] of water. Germany was the first to use submarines as warships. Its submarines were known as U-boats. Submarines were subsequently used by several other countries during World Wars I and II to attack enemy ships.

In 1954, the world's first nuclear-powered submarine, the *Nautilus,* was launched at Groton, Connecticut. It made further history in 1958 by becoming the first ship to sail under the North Pole.

*See also* SHIPS AND SHIPBUILDING. **PROJECT 4**

**MISSILE SUBMARINE**

The Polaris submarine (below) is nuclear powered. It can stay underwater for months at a time without refueling. The Polaris carries ballistic missiles.

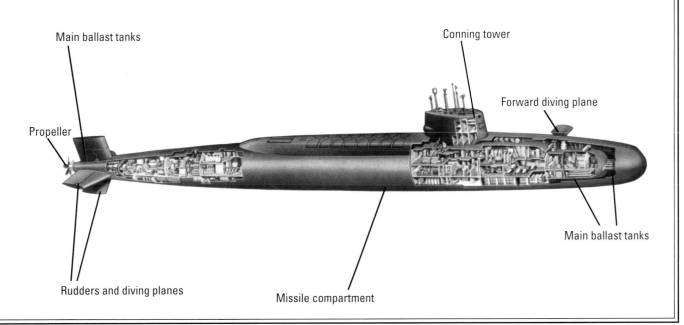

Main ballast tanks

Conning tower

Forward diving plane

Propeller

Main ballast tanks

Rudders and diving planes

Missile compartment

# SUBWAY

A subway is an underground railway system that runs on electricity. It provides rapid passenger service within a city and nearby areas. A subway is called the "tube" or the "underground" in England. In many places, it is known as the "metro."

Subways are usually built under city streets, but sometimes they are built under rivers too. Subways come aboveground in some cities—often in outlying areas. They are then known as elevated trains and are sometimes called "els."

Subway trains are usually made up of several passenger cars. Each car has its own electric motor and receives electricity for the motor from a third rail (see ELECTRIC MOTOR). This third rail is either in the center or at one side of the tracks. A device on the car called a shoe moves along this rail and conducts electricity from the rail to the motor. An operator in a small cab at the front of the lead car starts and stops the train at the stations along the route.

People called dispatchers in a central office watch a control board, which shows where every train is at any time. They make certain the trains move at the right speeds with set amounts of space between them for safety.

The world's first subway opened in London, England, in 1863. Steam locomotives were used at first. In 1890, the London subway switched to electric locomotives (see LOCOMOTIVE; STEAM ENGINE). Soon other major cities built electrically operated subways. Budapest, in Hungary, opened its subway in 1896; Paris, in France, opened its subway in 1898.

In the United States, Boston was the first city to have a subway, opening its line in 1897. It was 1.5 mi. [2.4 km] long. In 1904, New York City opened the first part of what later became the largest subway system in the world. Today, the New York subway system contains more than 235 mi. [378 km] of tracks. This system is so large that a person can ride from New Jersey, under New York City, beneath two rivers, to Long Island—all the while without once seeing daylight. Subways also operate in Philadelphia (opened in 1907), Chicago (opened in 1943), and Washington, D.C. (opened in 1980). One of the more modern subways is the inter-urban rapid-transit system known as BART (Bay Area Rapid Transit), completed in 1976 in San Francisco. BART's trains are fully automatic and can be run by computers (see COMPUTER).

In Canada, Toronto opened a subway in 1954, and Montreal opened one in 1966. Like the Paris subways, the Montreal trains use strong rubber tires on the wheels to cut down on noise. Cities throughout the world are introducing newer, more automatic equipment to make their subway systems more efficient and comfortable for their passengers.

*See also* RAILROAD.

**SUBWAY**
Subways are underground railroad systems that are powered by electricity. In many cities, such as Washington, D.C. (pictured), the subway system provides transportation for a large number of people going to and from work each day.

**SUCCESSION** (sək sĕsh′ən) The types of living organisms found in particular places change gradually over time. Such changes are called succession. Succession is a natural occurrence in the aging of an ecosystem (see ECOSYSTEM).

A very young ecosystem is the bare rock of a mountain. Nothing is able to live on it. As snow, ice, rain, and wind slowly break down the rock, certain species of algae, lichens, and mosses are able to grow on it (see ALGAE; LICHEN; MOSS, LIVERWORT, HORNWORT). These organisms continue the break down of the surface of the rock and cause small amounts of soil to form (see SOIL). The soil collects in cracks in the rock. Mites, springtails, and other small creatures live in the moss and in the forming soil. The seeds of small plants and trees fall into the cracks and begin to grow. These species are called pioneer species because they can live in an unfavorable environment (see ENVIRONMENT). Cedars and birches are common pioneer trees, or trees that appear first.

As the trees grow, their roots break apart the rock and cause more cracks where more plants can grow. The leaves fall to the ground and form humus (see HUMUS). Slowly, more soil is built up on top of the rock. Worms, mice, birds, and other small animals come to the area to feed on the plants and insects.

As the soil becomes deeper, other trees, such as maples and oaks, begin to grow. With more trees present, the soil forms faster. Soon a forest grows. Many species of animals make their homes in the forest. This final stage is often called the climax stage. Species of the climax stage usually completely replace the pioneer species. For example, birch trees cannot grow in the shade of a tall oak tree. The area has changed from bare rock to a mature oak forest. This succession, however, may take thousands of years.

Succession takes place in fresh water as well as on the land. As mud or silt and decaying plant remains build up on the bottom of a pond or lake, the water becomes shallower. The reeds and other plants that originally grew only in the shallows around the edge of the pond can then spread in toward the middle. As time goes by, more mud and debris accumulate on the bottom, and the reeds can then spread even further into the pond. The open water gradually disappears altogether, and what was once a pond becomes a reed swamp. Willows and other trees that grow near water soon move in and convert the swamp into damp woodland. The whole area gradually dries out, and other trees establish themselves. If humans do not interfere with the area, it will eventually turn into woodland. A small pond can be converted to woodland in less than fifty years. The exact composition of the final woodland will depend on the soil and the local climate.

**SUCCESSION**

Succession is the natural aging of an ecosystem. Here daisies—typical pioneer species—are growing in an abandoned part of a quarry.

**SUCKER** The word *sucker* applies to various types of attachment organs found in some organisms. Some parasites, for example, attach, or hold themselves, to their host by suckers (see PARASITE). The sucker of a parasitic plant may be a specialized root that gets inside the host tissues. Animal suckers are usually muscular disks that can exert suction.

Such disks often surround the mouth. The name *sucker* is also applied to the shoots that grow from the bases of roses and other woody plants. *Sucker* is also the name given to several kinds of fish. These fish usually have mouths with thick, fleshy lips that help them suck up food on the bottom of lakes and streams.

*See also* SUCKER (FISH).

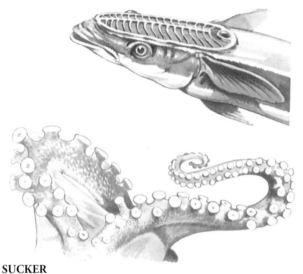

**SUCKER**

The remora fish (top) uses the sucker on its head to attach itself to larger fish. The arms of an octopus (bottom) have many suckers.

**SUCKER (FISH)** A sucker is a freshwater fish that belongs to the family Catostomidae. It is usually a long, slender fish with a tubelike mouth on the underside of its head. The sucker sucks insects, small crustaceans, and fish eggs off the bottom of a stream or lake (see CRUSTACEAN). It has no teeth.

Suckers are some of the most common fishes in North American streams. The white sucker usually reaches 19 in. [50 cm] in length. Several species of suckers have recently become rare.

**SUCROSE** (sōō′krōs′) Sucrose is the chemical name for common table sugar. It has the chemical formula $C_{12}H_{22}O_{11}$. Sucrose is found in the juice and stems of many plants. The most important commercial sources of sucrose are sugar cane and sugar beet. These plants are crushed and treated with water to get out the juice containing the sucrose. The juice is used to produce molasses, syrup, and sugar crystals. (The sugar crystals are separated from the syrup and refined.)

Sucrose is the cheapest pure chemical produced on a large scale. It is used by people to sweeten various foods and beverages. Sucrose is also used in the manufacture of many kinds of foods, such as jams and preserves. Chemically, sucrose is something like an alcohol. It forms esters with organic (carbon-containing) acids (see ALCOHOL; ESTER). Sucrose melts at 365°F [185°C] to form barley sugar. When heated to about 392°F [200°C], it forms caramel.

*See also* SUGAR.

**SUCTION** (sŭk′shən) Suction is the process of drawing liquids or gases into a space. This is done by sucking out or otherwise removing part of the air from the space, thereby reducing air pressure. The gas or liquid is then forced by atmospheric pressure into the space. Soda is drawn through a straw by suction. Suction is also used to lift small solid particles, as in the vacuum cleaner.

*See also* PRESSURE; VACUUM.

**SUCTORIAN** (sŭk tôr′ē ən) Suctorians are a type of protozoa (see PROTOZOA). The young suctorians are free swimming and have cilia that allow them to move through the water (see CILIUM). The adults are sessile (fixed to one spot) and do not have cilia. They usually attach themselves to surfaces underwater and grow long, hollow tentacles. These tentacles are used to capture, paralyze, and suck the body fluids from other protozoans and microorganisms (see MICROORGANISM). The suctorians usually reproduce by budding, though some cases of sexual reproduction have been observed (see

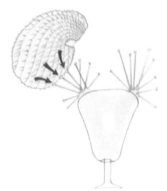

**SUCTORIAN**

Suctorians are protozoans that, as adults, have sucking tentacles. They use the tentacles to extract body fluids from other protozoans.

BUDDING; REPRODUCTION). Some suctorians are parasites. They may even be parasitic on other suctorians.

*See also* PARASITE.

## SUGAR

In chemistry, *sugar* is the name for a group of chemical compounds that are soluble (dissolvable) in water and have a sweet taste. Sugars are a type of carbohydrate (see CARBOHYDRATE; COMPOUND). Chemists call common table sugar *sucrose* ($C_{12}H_{22}O_{11}$) (see SUCROSE). By chemical methods, sucrose can be broken down into two other sugars. These sugars, called glucose and fructose, have a similar chemical makeup ($C_6H_{12}O_6$). Glucose is not as sweet as sucrose (see GLUCOSE). Fructose, also called levulose, is sweeter than sucrose. Like sucrose, glucose and fructose occur widely in nature.

Glucose and fructose are monosaccharides. Monosaccharides have molecules containing a basic ring of an oxygen atom and four or five carbon atoms with a hydroxyl group ($OH^-$) attached to each. Sucrose is a disaccharide. A disaccharide molecule contains two rings, formed by the combination of two monosaccharides with the removal of a molecule of water (see ATOM; MOLECULE).

In industry, many products are manufactured from sugar and its by-products. Some examples are nylon, various drugs, and monosodium glutamate. Monosodium glutamate is a substance used to bring out the flavor of food. ♘ PROJECT 18

## SUGAR BEET

The sugar beet is a biennial plant (living two years) that belongs to the goosefoot family (see BIENNIAL PLANT; GOOSEFOOT FAMILY). It is the second most important commercial source of sugar after sugar cane (see SUGAR CANE). The sugar beet is grown for its swollen, fleshy root, which may weigh more than 2.2 lb. [1 kg]. It contains 13 to 22 percent sugar.

At the top of the beet is a short stem called a crown. On top of the crown are bunches of long, narrow leaves. The leaves can be eaten as green vegetables. The crown is sometimes used as feed for livestock. After sugar has been taken from the sugar beet, a thick, dark syrup called molasses remains.

Molasses is used in cooking or as livestock feed. Sugar beet is grown in temperate areas throughout the world. The roots are usually harvested at the end of their first growing season.

*See also* SUGAR.

**SUGAR BEET**
These sugar beets have been dug out of the ground to show the fleshy roots, which contain up to 22 percent sugar.

## SUGAR CANE

Sugar cane is a tall grass plant that grows in tropical and semitropical regions (see GRASS). Sugar cane has thick stalks 10 to 15 ft. [3 to 5 m] in height and about 2 in. [5 cm] in diameter. These stalks contain a juice that is used to make sugar and syrup. The juice contains 10 to 20 percent sugar in the form of sucrose (see SUCROSE).

The stalks, or canes, of the sugar cane plant are crushed between heavy steel rollers. In this way, the juice is removed. The juice is then heated, filtered, and reduced to a syrup, from which sugar crystals

**SUGAR CANE**
Sugar cane is grown throughout the warm parts of the world for the juice in its stalks, which contain up to 20 percent sugar.

can be separated. India, Cuba, and Brazil are the largest producers of sugar cane.

*See also* SUGAR.

**SULFA DRUG** (sŭl′fə drŭg) Sulfa drugs are a type of drug used to treat diseases caused by bacteria and other microorganisms (see BACTERIA; DRUG; MICROORGANISM). Sulfa drugs are synthetic (human-made) chemicals. The first sulfa compound (mixture) was developed in 1908 and was used as a dye for wool cloth. It was not used as a medicine until the early 1930s. Gerhard Domagk, a German bacteriologist, thought that because some dyes stain, or stick to, bacteria, a poisonous dye would kill the bacteria. In 1932, he found that the dye called Prontosil killed *Streptococcus* bacteria. In 1935, Domagk isolated sulfanilamide as the active chemical in Prontosil. Since that time, scientists have experimented with over five thousand similar chemicals, but only about twenty of these can be used as medicines. These twenty compounds are all called sulfa drugs.

Sulfa drugs work by interfering with the normal metabolism of cells (see CELL; METABOLISM). All living cells need folic acid, a B vitamin, to grow and reproduce (see VITAMIN). Human beings and most other animals get folic acid from the food they eat. Bacteria and certain other microorganisms, however, make their own folic acid. In order to do this, they need a chemical called para-aminobenzoic acid (PABA). Chemically, sulfa drugs and PABA are almost the same. Sulfa drugs, however, have sulfur atoms, whereas PABA has no sulfur. Microorganisms cannot tell the difference between the two, and they absorb the sulfa drug. This prevents the production of folic acid. Without folic acid, the microorganisms cannot grow and reproduce. Thus, the sulfa drugs do not actually kill the microorganisms. Instead, they keep the microorganisms from reproducing. Then, the body's own defenses are able to kill the microorganisms.

Sulfa drugs do not affect all types of bacteria and other microorganisms that cause disease. They are effective in treating pneumonia and meningitis. However, they have little effect on such other diseases as tuberculosis. In addition, sulfa drugs are toxic—that is, they may cause poisoning or such side effects as nausea or skin blisters. In addition, many types of microorganisms have developed a resistance to sulfa drugs, because the drugs have been used so widely.

New, more effective, and less toxic drugs have replaced many of the sulfa drugs. Although sulfa drugs are still used to treat certain diseases, many diseases are more effectively controlled by antibiotics (see ANTIBIOTIC). The use of sulfa drugs and antibiotics has saved thousands of lives and has been a major factor in the control of infectious diseases.

*See also* DISEASE; IMMUNITY.

**SULFATE** (sŭl′fāt′) Sulfates are salts of sulfuric acid (see SALTS; SULFURIC ACID). The formula for sulfuric acid is $H_2SO_4$. Sulfates are formed when the hydrogen atoms (H) of sulfuric acid are replaced by metal atoms. The hydrogen atoms can also be replaced by groups of atoms such as the ammonium group ($NH_4^+$). Important sulfates include ammonium sulfate (($NH_4)_2SO_4$) and sodium sulfate ($Na_2SO_4$). Ammonium sulfate is used as a fertilizer. Several minerals are sulfates. An example is gypsum, which is calcium sulfate.

*See also* FERTILIZER; GYPSUM; MINERAL.

**SULFIDE** (sŭl′fīd′) Sulfides are compounds of sulfur with one other element (see COMPOUND; ELEMENT; SULFUR). An important sulfide is the gas hydrogen sulfide ($H_2S$) (see HYDROGEN SULFIDE). Many minerals consist of sulfides (see MINERAL). Examples are galena (lead sulfide) and iron pyrites (iron sulfide). Metallic sulfides can sometimes be made by heating the metal in the presence of sulfur. Another common method is to pass hydrogen sulfide through a solution of a salt of the metal. Since most metal sulfides are insoluble—that is, they do not dissolve—the sulfide is formed as a solid mass in the solution. This is called a precipitate (see PRECIPITATE; SALTS). Some metal sulfides are brightly colored and are used as pigments (coloring substances). For example, the red pigment vermillion is mercury sulfide. An important nonmetallic sulfide is carbon disulfide ($CS_2$). Carbon disulfide is widely used as a solvent (substance that dissolves other substances) in industry.

**SULFITE** (sŭl'fīt´) Sulfites are salts of sulfurous acid. The formula for sulfurous acid is $H_2SO_3$. A sulfite is formed when the hydrogen atoms (H) are replaced by metal atoms. Sulfites all contain the sulfite ion ($SO_3^{2-}$). They are made by dissolving sulfur dioxide in solutions, bases, or carbonates of the metal (see IONS AND IONIZATION; SALTS; SULFUR DIOXIDE).

Sulfites are used as bleaching agents. Sulfites are also used in foods as preservatives and to prevent discoloration. However, some people are allergic to sulfites. Therefore, the Food and Drug Administration (FDA) has banned the use of sulfites on all fresh fruits and vegetables sold in the United States. The FDA also requires that processed foods containing sulfites must list these ingredients on the label.

**SULFUR** (sŭl'fər) Sulfur is an important non-metallic element. It is found in several different forms called allotropes (see ALLOTROPE; ELEMENT). The most common allotrope of sulfur is called rhombic sulfur. It is made up of yellow, eight-sided crystals (see CRYSTAL). When it is heated to more than 204°F [95°C], it changes into another form called monoclinic sulfur. Monoclinic sulfur is made up of fine, needlelike yellow crystals. Another allotrope of sulfur is made by pouring molten (melted) sulfur into cold water. The sulfur becomes a solid, a tough brown-yellow mass called plastic sulfur. At normal temperatures, both monoclinic and plastic sulfur slowly change into rhombic sulfur. Another allotrope is called flowers of sulfur. It is a yellow powder and is made by quickly cooling sulfur vapor (see VAPOR).

Large deposits of sulfur are found beneath the ground, especially in the United States. Sulfur is mined by a method called the Frasch process. Superheated water and compressed air are pumped down to the sulfur. Superheated water is water that is at a temperature above its boiling point but is still liquid. The sulfur melts and is forced up to the surface in pipes. Sulfur also occurs in nature in many different compounds (see COMPOUND). It is taken from the gas hydrogen sulfide, which is found in natural gas and coal gas (see HYDROGEN SULFIDE). It is also taken from metal sulfide ores such as iron pyrites. Sulfur also occurs as sulfates in such minerals as gypsum, which is calcium sulfate (see SULFATE; SULFIDE).

Most sulfur is used to make sulfuric acid, an important chemical in many industries (see SULFURIC ACID). Sulfur also is used to make wood pulp

**SULFUR**
Melted sulfur mined by the Frasch process is run into huge tanks and left to harden. It is then dug out by machines, mostly for making sulfuric acid.

and to vulcanize rubber (see VULCANIZATION). It is used to make a wide range of products such as drugs, dyes, and chemicals to kill insects and molds. Sulfur is also used in gunpowder and in making matches.

Sulfur is a reactive element. It burns in air with a blue flame to form the gas sulfur dioxide, which is a dangerous part of air pollution (see POLLUTION; SULFUR DIOXIDE).

Sulfur's atomic number is 16. Its relative atomic mass is 32.06. It melts at 246°F [119°C] and boils at 832°F [444°C]. Its relative density is 2. *See also* RELATIVE DENSITY.

**SULFUR DIOXIDE** (sŭl'fər dī ŏk'sīd') Sulfur dioxide ($SO_2$) is a colorless, poisonous gas with a strong odor. It is made by heating sulfur in air. It is also made by roasting sulfide ores, such as iron pyrites, in air (see SULFIDE; SULFUR). Many industrial processes produce sulfur dioxide as a waste product. The air in cities is usually polluted with sulfur dioxide. It dissolves in rainwater to form a compound called sulfurous acid. Sulfurous acid is destructive because it slowly eats away the mortar and marble in buildings. It is also one of the main components in acid rain (see ACID RAIN: POLLUTION).

Sulfur dioxide is used in industry to make sulfuric acid, which is a very important chemical (see SULFURIC ACID). Sulfur dioxide is also used to make sulfites (see SULFITE). Liquid sulfur dioxide is used in some refrigerators.

**SULFURIC ACID** (sŭl fyŏŏr'ĭk ăs'ĭd) Sulfuric acid ($H_2SO_4$) is one of the most important chemicals used in industry. It is used in producing superphosphate and ammonium sulfate fertilizers (see FERTILIZER). Metals are placed in baths of sulfuric acid to clean them. Sulfuric acid is also used in refining sugar and petroleum, in automobile batteries, and in producing a vast range of chemicals including detergents, dyes, and medicines.

Pure sulfuric acid is a heavy, oily, colorless liquid. It is very reactive and attacks most metals to form salts called sulfates (see SULFATE). Pure sulfuric acid quickly absorbs water and is often used as a drying agent. *See also* ACID; SULFUR.

**SUMAC** (sōō'măk') The sumacs are a group of more than one hundred deciduous shrubs and small trees that belong to genus *Rhus* of the cashew family. They are native to temperate and subtropical areas. They have large divided leaves (see LEAF). The small flowers grow in clusters at the ends of branches.

Among the best known sumacs are poison ivy, poison oak, and poison sumac. These and many other sumacs are poisonous plants and may cause rashes, blisters, and other skin irritations if they are handled (see POISONOUS PLANT).

Staghorn sumac is a common tree in North America. It reaches a height of 36 ft. [11 m] and has green flowers and red berries. The younger branches or twigs are furry. The leaves become bright red in the fall, making it a favorite garden tree.

**SUMAC**

There are more than one hundred kinds of sumacs, some of which are poisonous. Pictured right is the sugar sumac, which grows in North America.

The sun is the closest star to the earth (see STAR). The sun is directly responsible for all life on Earth. It provides the earth with almost all of its light, heat, and other energy.

The sun is also the center of our solar system. The planets, including the earth, all follow paths, called orbits, around the sun (see PLANET; SOLAR SYSTEM).

## Solar statistics

The sun lies about 93 million mi. [150 million km] from the earth. The sun has a diameter of 865,000 mi. [1,392,000 km]—about 109 times the earth's diameter. The sun's volume is about 1.3 million times larger than that of the earth (see VOLUME). This means that the sun could contain 1.3 million earths inside of it. However, the sun is considered only a medium-sized star.

The sun moves in two ways. It makes a complete rotation on its axis (an imaginary line running through its center, from pole to pole) about once a month. The sun, together with other members of the solar system, also revolves around the center of the Milky Way galaxy (see MILKY WAY). It takes the sun about 225 million years to make one complete revolution.

The sun makes up more than 99 percent of the total mass of the solar system (see MASS). Because of its gigantic size, the sun has a much stronger gravitational field than the planets do (see GRAVITY). A person would weigh about twenty-eight times more on the sun than on the earth.

## Solar structure

The sun is made of about 75 percent hydrogen, almost 25 percent helium, and traces of about seventy other elements (see ELEMENT; HELIUM; HYDROGEN). The hottest part of the sun is its core, or center. The temperature there is about 27,000,000°F [15,000,000°C]. The nuclear reactions that produce the sun's energy occur at the core. The middle third of the sun's interior, surrounding the core, is called the radiative zone. The temperature

### SUN'S STRUCTURE

The sun has a dense, hot core surrounded by layers in which material moves to the surface. The chromosphere and the corona lie above the photosphere, which is the surface we can see.

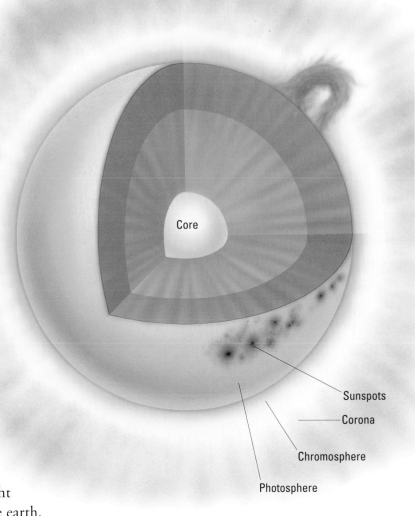

Core

Sunspots

Corona

Chromosphere

Photosphere

there is between 5,580,000 to 11,700,000°F [3,100,000 to 6,500,000°C].

The convection zone is the outermost third of the sun's interior, ending just below the sun's surface. The temperature in the convection zone is around 2,000,000°F [1,100,000°C]. Solar energy passing through the convection zone is subjected to much turbulence. This turbulence may help transmit energy to the sun's surface.

*Photosphere* is the name for the sun's surface. The temperature there is about 10,800°F [6,000°C]. The sun's heat and light are given off from the photosphere. The photosphere is about 340 mi. [550 km] thick and includes the innermost layer of the sun's atmosphere.

Above the photosphere is a region of high temperatures known as the chromosphere. The chromosphere is the central layer of the solar atmosphere. The temperature of the chromosphere averages about 18,000°F [10,000°C]. The outer region of the sun's atmosphere is called the corona. The temperatures there are near 2,700,000°F [1,500,000°C] (see CORONA).

## Solar energy production

Like most other stars, the sun produces energy by transforming hydrogen into helium. Through a series of complex nuclear reactions, hydrogen atoms fuse to form helium atoms. This reaction releases a tremendous amount of energy (see FUSION).

## Solar activity

Spectacular events occur on the sun's surface and in its atmosphere. These include prominences, sunspots, spicules, and solar flares. All these activities are caused to some degree by changes in the sun's magnetic field (see MAGNETISM). The magnetic field is usually relatively constant at the sun's poles. At the solar equator (an imaginary line running around the middle of the sun), however, the magnetic field is in a state of constant change. When changes in the magnetic field occur, violent solar activity takes place.

A prominence is a huge, dense region of gas that forms as high as 622,000 mi. [1,000,000 km] above the sun's surface. Some prominences appear as great arches following magnetic lines of force.

They usually die out soon after they form. Less dramatic prominences, called quiescent (quiet) prominences, may last several weeks.

Sunspots appear as dark spots on the sun's surface (see SUNSPOT). Sunspots are cooler than the surrounding area. The inner part of a sunspot is called the umbra, and the lighter, outer part is called the penumbra.

Sunspots occur where magnetic lines of force intersect the surface of the sun. They seem to occur in cycles of eleven years. At the beginning of the sunspot cycle, sunspots appear near the solar latitudes of 30°. Eventually, they appear closer and closer to the solar equator.

Spicules are ejections of gas that extend from the chromosphere to the corona. Intense eruptions associated with sunspots are called solar flares. Solar flares produce streams of charged particles that reach the earth in about one day. This stream of particles, called the solar wind, disrupts radio communications and causes brilliant aurora displays on the earth (see AURORA; SOLAR WIND).

## The sun and the earth

The sun provides the earth with visible light and ultraviolet and infrared rays. It also emits radio waves and X rays. The full impact of all of this radiation would be very dangerous on Earth. However, the earth is shielded from most of the dangerous radiation by its atmosphere (see ATMOSPHERE; RADIATION).

Scientists study the sun to learn how other stars function. One of the best times to study the sun is during a total solar eclipse. During such an event, the moon blocks out the sun so just its outer atmosphere is visible. Phenomena such as solar prominences are evident during total eclipses (see ECLIPSE).

The sun is observed through special solar telescopes, which reflect the sun's image into an observing room. The United States has sent several probes into outer space to perform experiments and make observations of the sun. These space probes have added valuable knowledge to our understanding of the sun.

*See also* SPACE EXPLORATION; STAR; TELESCOPE.

 PROJECT 51

**SUN BEAR** The sun bear is the smallest of the bears. It is usually about 3.3 ft. [1 m] long and weighs less than 140 lb. [65 kg]. This bear, which lives in Asia, has black fur with yellow or white markings on its chest. These markings inspired people to name the bear the sun bear. The sun bear is sometimes called the Malayan bear or the honey bear.

The sun bear has large paws with long, curved claws. These claws help it dig in the ground in search of insects and other small animals, which it eats. The sun bear also feeds on plants, fruits, and honey. It spends most of its time in trees, using its curved claws to climb and hold on to tree branches. *See also* BEAR.

**SUNDIAL** A sundial is an instrument used to measure time. It is the most ancient time-telling device used by humans. The Babylonians used sundials four thousand years ago.

Sundials are made up of a plane (dial face) and a gnomon (style). The plane is divided into hours, usually from 5 A.M. to 8 P.M., the hours when the sun is shining. On a horizontal sundial, the gnomon is a piece of metal fixed in the center of the plane. It points toward the North Pole in the

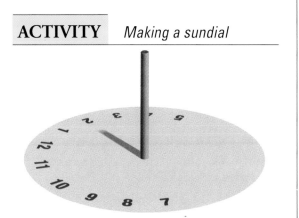

**ACTIVITY** *Making a sundial*

Cut a circle of poster board 6 in. [15 cm] in diameter. Push a pencil through the center. Take your sundial outside at noon on a sunny day and mark "12" opposite the shadow of the pencil. Then mark "1," "2," "3," and so on, every hour until the evening. The following morning, mark the hours up to noon. If you take your sundial indoors, you can replace it correctly by using a compass to align the noon position with north.

Northern Hemisphere and the South Pole in the Southern Hemisphere. The gnomon is set at an angle equal to the latitude of the sundial's location (see LATITUDE AND LONGITUDE; POLE).

On a vertical sundial, the gnomon is fixed at the upper edge of the plane. When the sun shines on a sundial, the gnomon casts a shadow that points to the correct time. Most sundials today are not used for telling time but instead serve as ornaments in gardens.

**SUNFISH** This name is given to two very different groups of fishes. The best known are the freshwater sunfishes that belong to the family Centrarchidae. These are thin but deep-bodied fishes with spiny fins, large eyes, and often

**SUNDIAL**

The shadow of the gnomon on this vertical sundial indicates that the time is nearly half past two.

**SUNFISH**

The sunfish is fairly small but popular with fishers because it puts up a strong fight when hooked.

a small mouth. Many sunfishes are very colorful.

There are many species of sunfishes, including the basses and the crappies (see BASS; CRAPPIE). The bluegill is probably the best-known species of sunfish. The sunfishes are popular game fishes because they will strike lures as well as live bait, and they put up a strong fight. Most sunfishes rarely grow longer than 10 in. [25 cm]. The sunfishes are native to North America, but they have been introduced to many other parts of the world.

The ocean sunfish, belonging to the family Molidae, is an unusual marine fish. It has no tail and such a short body that it looks just like a large head swimming through the water. This fish grows up to 10 ft. [3 m] long and weighs up to 1.5 tons [1,400 kg]. Large paddlefish fins drive the fish through the water. Ocean sunfishes live in warm and temperate seas all over the world.

**SUNFLOWER** Sunflowers are annual plants that belong to genus *Helianthus* of the composite family (see ANNUAL PLANT; COMPOSITE FAMILY; PERENNIAL PLANT). They have rough, simple, heart-shaped leaves and hairy stems (see LEAF). Large flower heads grow at the tips of the stems and are made of many disk and ray florets. The disk (center) florets may be yellow, brown, or purple.

The ray (petallike) florets are usually yellow. The flower head may be more than 1 ft. [30 cm] in diameter (see FLOWER).

Some sunflower varieties reach a height of 15 ft. [4.5 m] and are popular garden plants. Other varieties are grown on a large scale in Europe and Canada for their seeds. Sunflower seeds are sometimes used as feed for livestock. The seeds yield a high-quality cooking oil. The seeds are also popular as a human food and can be eaten raw or roasted. They are also used to make breads and a coffeelike beverage.

**SUNSPOT** A sunspot is a dark marking that appears on the sun's surface. Sunspots are several thousand degrees cooler than the surrounding area of the sun. The inner part of a sunspot is called the umbra. The lighter, outer part of a sunspot is called the penumbra. Small sunspots with no penumbrae (plural of *penumbra*) are called pores.

Sunspots occur where lines of magnetic force intersect the sun's surface (see MAGNETISM). Sunspots range in size from 600 mi. [1,000 km] to about 25,000 mi. [40,000 km] in width. Small sunspots may last for only a few hours or days. Larger sunspots may remain on the sun's surface for months.

Sunspots seem to occur in eleven-year cycles.

**SUNFLOWER**

Sunflowers have flower heads that may grow to be more than 1 ft. [30 cm] in diameter. The heads produce seeds that are used as food for livestock and humans.

**SUNSPOT**

A spray of material flies outward from the sun's surface at a sunspot. The photograph at right was taken by the solar telescope on board *Skylab*, the first manned orbiting observatory.

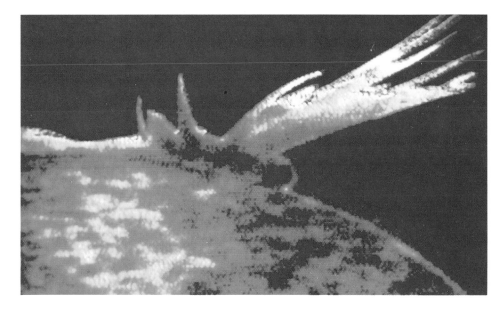

The cycle usually begins with groups of sunspots appearing near the solar latitudes of 30°. The sunspots then migrate toward the solar equator. Solar activity is most intense during the height of the sunspot cycle.

The earth's magnetic field is often disturbed by sunspot activity. Sunspots cause disruptions in radio communications and generate auroral displays in the sky.

*See also* AURORA; SOLAR WIND; SUN.

# SUPERCONDUCTIVITY (soo´pər kŏn´dŭk tĭv´ĭ tē) Superconductivity is the absence of resistance to electric current that can exist in some metals, alloys (combinations of metals), and certain other materials (see ALLOY; CURRENT, ELECTRIC; METAL AND METALLURGY; RESISTANCE, ELECTRICAL). Materials that are not superconductive can still conduct electricity (see CONDUCTION OF ELECTRICITY). For example, aluminum, copper, and gold at normal temperatures are good conductors of electricity. However, even good conductors have some resistance to electricity. This resistance causes a certain amount of the electrical energy to be lost in the form of heat. Devices that are made of these materials, such as wire, then have some inefficiency (see EFFICIENCY).

This fact prompted scientists to research how to reduce, or even eliminate, electrical resistance so that no electricity is wasted. The property of superconductivity was first discovered in 1911. At that time, materials had to be cooled to nearly -459.67°F [-273.15°C], which is absolute zero, for superconductivity to be achieved (see ABSOLUTE ZERO). This was done by immersing materials, such as the element mercury, in helium that had been cooled so that it liquefied (see ELEMENT; MERCURY). The liquid helium in turn cooled the materials close enough to absolute zero to make them superconductive (see HELIUM).

The problem with this method is that liquid helium is expensive and difficult to work with. In the 1980s, however, scientists discovered materials, such as certain ceramics, that became superconductive at warmer temperatures. Certain ceramics become superconductive at -234°F [-148°C] or above. Scientists also discovered that liquid nitrogen

**SUPERCONDUCTIVITY**

A small magnet floats above a superconducting ceramic material cooled by liquid nitrogen.

could be used instead of liquid helium for cooling (see CERAMICS; NITROGEN). Liquid nitrogen is less expensive than liquid helium and easier to work with.

The discovery of materials that are superconductive at temperatures warmer than absolute zero will have far-reaching consequences. Scientists are researching how such devices as computers, electric locomotives, and electric power lines could become superefficient in their operation by having components made of superconducting materials. Scientists hope to one day find materials that are superconductive at room temperature.

*See also* CRYOGENICS.

## SUPERCOOLING

When a particular liquid is cooled to a certain temperature, it becomes a solid (see STATES OF MATTER). This temperature is called the liquid's freezing point (see FREEZING AND FREEZING POINT). Liquids usually contain small amounts of solid impurities, such as dust. When the liquid is cooled, it first solidifies around these impurities. If the liquid is completely free of solid impurities, it may not freeze at its regular freezing point. The liquid is then said to be supercooled. If the liquid is shaken, or if solid particles are added, the liquid quickly becomes solid. Supercooling is an important factor in precipitation.

*See also* PRECIPITATION.

## SUPERNOVA

A supernova is a violently exploding star. A supernova occurs when a star more massive than our sun runs out of fuel and explodes. The star may increase in brightness by more than twenty magnitudes during the explosion (see MAGNITUDE; STAR).

Astronomers believe that when a large star runs out of fuel, its core quickly collapses. The energy released during the collapse causes the star to explode (see ASTRONOMY; NUCLEAR ENERGY). A supernova reaches a brightness billions of times that of the sun within a few days of the explosion. The remains of the exploded star form either a neutron star or a black hole (see BLACK HOLE; NEUTRON STAR).

In 1054, Chinese astronomers recorded the supernova that formed the Crab Nebula (see CRAB NEBULA). Other supernovae were observed in 1572 and 1604. In 1987, a supernova was observed about 163,000 light-years away, in a nearby galaxy (see GALAXY; LIGHT-YEAR).

The supernova that occurred in 1987 was the first supernova visible to the naked eye since 1604. Telescopes on satellites have recorded X rays, infrared rays, and ultraviolet rays from that supernova (see SATELLITE; TELESCOPE). Astronomers are searching for a neutron star or a pulsar at the core of the 1987 supernova (see PULSAR).

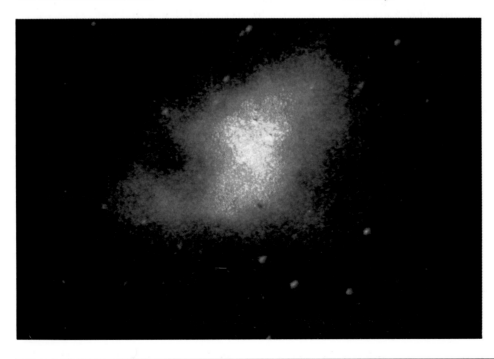

**SUPERNOVA**

The Crab Nebula (left) is the rapidly expanding remains of a supernova that exploded in 1054.

**SUPERSONIC FLIGHT**

The Anglo-French *Concorde* is a supersonic airliner that can carry one hundred passengers between London and New York City in about three hours.

**SUPERSONIC FLIGHT** Aircraft that fly faster than the speed of sound are said to be supersonic. The speed of sound at sea level is about 765 m.p.h. [1,190 kph]. The speed of sound decreases as the altitude increases, so that at 35,000 ft. [10,500 m], the speed of sound is only about 660 m.p.h. [1,060 kph] (see SOUND).

Engineers and pilots use Mach numbers to describe the speed of aircraft flying near or above the speed of sound. A Mach number is found by dividing the speed of the airplane by the speed of sound at the plane's altitude (see MACH). Mach 1 is the speed of sound, Mach 2 is twice the speed of sound, and so on. Flight speed slower than Mach 1 is called subsonic flight.

Aircraft flying near or above the speed of sound produce shock waves. Shock waves are waves of pressure that travel out from the moving aircraft (see SHOCK WAVE). When these waves reach the earth, they are sometimes heard as loud explosions, or sonic booms. Sometimes, sonic booms can break windows and cause other damage to property. Aircraft designers try to prevent or lessen the number of sonic booms by carefully streamlining supersonic aircraft (see STREAMLINING). Most supersonic aircraft have sharp, pointed noses and small, swept-back wings with sharp front edges. Planes that fly at speeds over 960 m.p.h. [1,600 kph] must have outer skins made of titanium or stainless steel to protect them against heat caused by the friction of high-speed flight (see FRICTION).

Many of today's military planes can fly at supersonic speeds. The best-known supersonic plane in the world is probably the *Concorde*. It is a passenger-carrying airliner designed and built by British and French companies. The *Concorde* can fly across the Atlantic Ocean from London to New York City in about three hours. Subsonic passenger jets take about twice that time.

*See also* AERODYNAMICS; AIRPLANE.

**SURFACE AREA** The surface area of any solid is the total area of all of its faces. A cube has six square faces. Its surface area is the sum of these, $6x^2$, where $x$ is the length of one of its sides. There are different formulas that are used to determine the surface area of many solids, such as a sphere or a right circular cone. In nature, the surface area of many objects has important consequences, especially when considering the ratio between surface area and volume (see RATIO). An animal that is twice the size of another will have roughly eight times the volume and mass but only four times the surface area. This means that any processes that depend on surface area (such as heat loss) will occur only half as easily in the larger animal.

**SURFACE TENSION** Surface tension is a force that occurs at the surface of a liquid. The molecules in a liquid are held together by a force (see MOLECULE; STATES OF MATTER). For molecules inside the liquid, this force acts from all sides. However, for a molecule on the surface, the force only acts from one side, the side where the liquid is. Therefore, the molecules on the surface are attracted down into the liquid. This causes surface tension. It makes the surface of the liquid act like

an elastic (flexible) film. This film can support light objects. For example, a needle will remain on the surface of a bowl of water if the needle is placed carefully. If the needle is disturbed, it will sink.

Raising the temperature of a liquid or dissolving substances in the liquid affects the surface tension. For example, soap and detergent lower the surface tension of water. **PROJECT 19**

**SURFACE WATER** *Surface water* generally refers to water on the surface of the earth, such as lakes, oceans, rivers, and streams. In contrast, groundwater is water beneath the earth's surface (see GROUNDWATER).

Surface water may be either fresh water or salt water. Surface water is continually being replenished through the water cycle (see WATER CYCLE).

Surface water has many uses. It is used by humans for irrigation, for drinking water, for recreation, and as a source of power (see HYDRO-ELECTRIC POWER; IRRIGATION). Unfortunately, surface water is being polluted by such things as improperly treated sewage and petroleum (oil) spills. This means that the amount of surface water fit for certain uses, such as drinking, is decreasing.

*See also* POLLUTION; SEWAGE TREATMENT; WATER; WATER SUPPLY.

**SURFACE WATER**

Water in lakes, oceans, rivers, and streams is called surface water. This is in contrast to groundwater, which is located beneath the earth's surface.

**SURGERY** (sûr′jə rē) Surgery is the branch of medicine that treats disease, deformities, or injuries by operations (see MEDICINE). An operation usually requires cutting into the body. A doctor who performs operations is called a surgeon. Every physician has some training in surgery and can perform simple operations. However, a physician who is a surgeon is specially trained to have the judgment and skill necessary to perform complex and difficult operations.

A little more than a hundred years ago, surgery was extremely dangerous to patients. It was performed only in absolute emergencies. Many patients who underwent surgery died, often through loss of blood, shock, or as a result of disease-causing microorganisms entering the body by way of the cut made by the surgeon (see INFECTION; SHOCK). A better understanding of the body's

**SURGERY**

Surgeons are physicians who have had the special training necessary to perform complex and difficult operations. Surgery usually requires cutting into the body to treat diseases, deformities, and injuries.

functions and of the causes of infection and disease has helped make surgery much safer today.

**The surgeon at work** Except in cases of emergency, all but very simple surgical operations happen in a special operating room in a hospital. A surgical team, usually made up of a surgeon, a first assistant, an anesthesiologist, and a nurse, perform routine operations. All scrub their hands thoroughly and wear sterile clothing, including gowns, face masks, and rubber gloves. The operating room and all the equipment are sterilized (see STERILIZATION). This is done to minimize the number of disease-causing microorganisms (which could enter the patient's body during the operation) in the area around the patient (see ASEPSIS).

The anesthesiologist prepares the patient for the operation by giving the patient sedatives and an anesthetic, or drug that causes a loss of feeling (see ANESTHETIC; SEDATIVE). In many operations, a general anesthetic is used to put the patient to sleep. In some cases, a local anesthetic is used. A local anesthetic affects only the nerves in the area

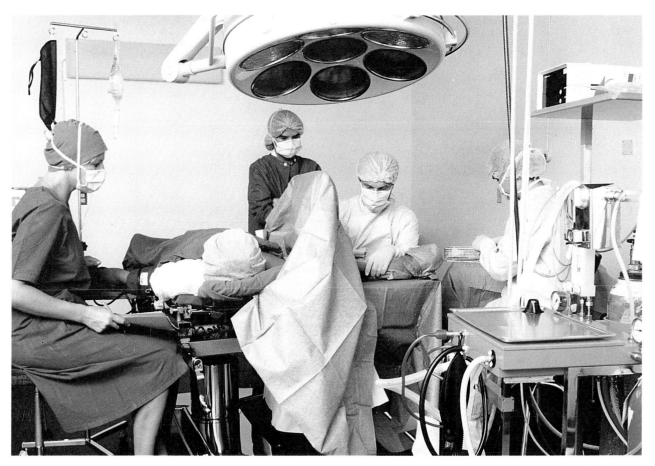

near where it is applied, so that only part of the body is made numb. If a general anesthetic is used, the anesthesiologist watches the patient's level of unconsciousness throughout the operation. The anesthesiologist also must check the patient's heartbeat and breathing rate to see that they are normal. Stimulant drugs and resuscitation machines are available if necessary (see STIMULANT).

A surgeon may use many tools or instruments during an operation. Sharp instruments, such as scissors and scalpels (knives) are used to make an incision (opening) in the patient's body. Other instruments include holders for needles and sponges, clamps to close off blood vessels, and retractors to hold back folds of skin. Sponges, which are actually pieces of gauze made into small pads, are used to remove any surplus blood. Some operations require saws to cut through bones. Equipment for giving blood transfusions is also available (see BLOOD TRANSFUSION). Surgeons may also use lasers for some kinds of surgery, such as operating on the eyes, destroying tumors (abnormal growths), breaking up urinary bladder stones, and clearing cholesterol blockages in the arteries of the heart (see LASER). For some operations, surgeons use fiber optic devices (endoscopes) that are inserted into the body through narrow tubes. Endoscopes allow them to see and operate on internal organs without making large cuts (see ENDOSCOPY; FIBER OPTICS).

At the end of the operation, cut tissues are usually put back together by sewing the edges together with sutures (special threads). In some cases, special clips are used. In time, the cut edges grow together again. The outside sutures are then removed. The inside sutures dissolve or are absorbed by the body.

### Kinds of surgery

A common operation may involve removal of a diseased part of the body. The medical name of such an operation generally ends in -ectomy. For example, an appendectomy is the removal of the appendix (see APPENDIX). A tonsillectomy is the removal of the tonsils (see TONSIL). Another common type of operation is the removal of an obstruction, such as a kidney stone. Amputation is the removal of a limb or part of a limb, or some other part of the body.

Surgery is often used to repair torn tissues or to rebuild tissues that have been destroyed. People with certain disorders may have a small machine placed in their body to help a certain organ work (see MEDICAL ENGINEERING; PACEMAKER). Sometimes, an organ taken from the body of one person may be placed, or transplanted, into another person (see TRANSPLANT; TRANSPLANTATION). Cryosurgery makes use of extreme cold. It often involves freezing tissues (see CRYOGENICS). Microsurgery (surgery performed on tiny parts under high magnification) enables surgeons to reattach severed limbs, as well as to weld a detached retina to the eye. Using a special microscope, surgeons can operate even on the tiny bones of the inner ear to cure a hearing disorder called conduction deafness (see EAR; EYE AND VISION).

Many surgeons specialize in one type of surgery. Ophthalmology is a specialty in treating diseases of the eyes. Plastic surgery is a specialty that repairs and rebuilds body tissues (see PLASTIC SURGERY). Other specialties include brain surgery and heart surgery. In all fields of surgery, new knowledge and techniques continue to bring much progress.

**SURVIVAL OF THE FITTEST** This expression was first used by the British naturalist Charles Darwin when he was developing his theory of evolution by means of natural selection (see DARWIN, CHARLES; EVOLUTION; NATURAL SELECTION). Living things are always competing with each other for food and other necessities of life. Darwin pointed out that only the fittest individuals of a species can survive the competition. In this context, the fittest ones are those that are best equipped for a particular environment (see ENVIRONMENT). The fittest individuals might be better at finding food, better at hiding from or escaping from their enemies, or better able to deal with drought or cold. Individuals that are less able to deal with the environment are more likely to die. This kind of competition goes on in each generation. Because only the fittest individuals survive and pass on their successful characteristics to their offspring, the population gradually improves and becomes increasingly better adapted to its environment. In other words, the population evolves.

**SUSPENSION** (sə spĕn′shən) A suspension is a mixture of a liquid or a gas and very small particles of solid matter. The particles stay dispersed (evenly distributed) throughout the liquid and do not settle. Mud is a suspension of soil particles in water. When one liquid is dispersed in another liquid—for example, oil in water—the result is an emulsion.

*See also* COLLOID; EMULSION; SOLUTION AND SOLUBILITY.

**SWALLOW** A swallow is a small bird that belongs to the family Hirundinidae. Swallows have long, pointed wing and often a deeply forked tail. The bill is short but well adapted for catching flying insects, the swallow's main food item. Swallows are usually between 4 and 6 in. [9 and 15 cm] in length.

There are several species of swallows native to North America. Swallows are often seen in large numbers, darting back and forth in the air, feeding on insects. They also perch together on telephone wires or trees, especially when preparing to fly

**SWALLOW**

The barn swallow is found in North America and Europe. The American race of barn swallow (top left) has brighter colors than its European cousin. Barn swallows build nests of mud (top right) and raise up to eight young, which they feed insects.

south in the fall (see MIGRATION). They nest in barns, on the sides of cliffs, under bridges, or in holes in trees or in the banks of streams.

**SWAMP CYPRESS** The swamp cypress is a coniferous tree that, unlike most conifers, is deciduous (see CONIFER; DECIDUOUS TREE). Swamp cypresses grow in swampy areas of the United States. These trees have a tapering trunk that may be 100 ft. [30 m] tall. The roots grow underwater. They have knobby growths called knees that grow up above the water and probably absorb air. The swamp cypress is also known as the bald cypress.

**SWAMP CYPRESS**

Swamp cypresses are unusual among cone-bearing trees because they are deciduous—they lose their leaves in winter.

**SWAN** A swan is a large, usually white water bird that belongs to the family Anatidae. It is closely related to ducks and geese. The swan has a long, heavy bill; long, slender neck; long wings; and short, stocky legs with webbed feet. It spends much of its time paddling in calm waters, feeding on plants growing on, or just below, the surface. A swan is a strong flier but has trouble getting into the air. It must paddle along the water surface for a time to build up speed before being able to take off.

**SWAN**
The black-necked swan, shown here (far left) carrying two cygnets (chicks) on its back, is a native of South America. The whooper swan (left) is all white, like other species of swans from the Northern Hemisphere.

There are three species of swans in North America. The tundra swan, which grows to a length of 36 in. [90 cm], nests in the Arctic. During the winter and while migrating, this swan is found throughout much of western Canada and the northern United States (see MIGRATION). The American race of the tundra swan is also called the whistling swan. The trumpeter swan is the largest species, growing to a length of 44 in. [112 cm] with a wingspan of about 95 in. [240 cm]. Although this species almost became extinct, its numbers are now increasing under the protection of the United States and Canadian governments (see EXTINCTION). The trumpeter swan has been reintroduced into a number of western lakes in the northwestern United States and Canada.

The mute swan was introduced to North America from Europe. It is the most familiar of the swans, as it is commonly seen in park lakes and ponds. The mute swan has spread along the northeastern coast of North America and is sometimes a nuisance to land owners and boaters because of its aggressive nature. It can be distinguished from the other swans when swimming because it usually bends its neck back in a graceful curve.

**SWEAT GLAND** (swĕt glănd) Perspiration, or sweating, is the loss of a watery fluid from tiny glands in the skin. This watery fluid is called sweat and is produced by sweat glands. The human body has about three million sweat glands. They are especially numerous in the armpits and on the

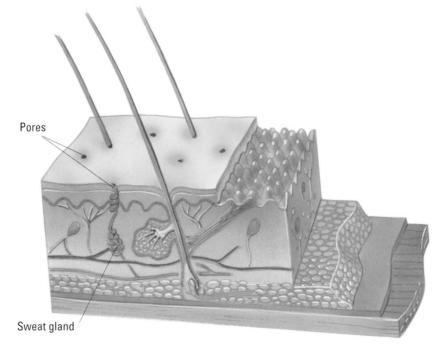

**SWEAT GLAND**

Sweat is produced by sweat glands and released through pores in the skin. There are about three million sweat glands in a human's skin.

Pores

Sweat gland

forehead, the palms of the hands, and the soles of the feet.

Sweating is a form of excretion (see EXCRETION). It helps rid the body of waste products, such as salt. The main purpose of sweating, however, is to help control body temperature (see TEMPERATURE, BODY). When sweat evaporates, it carries heat from the body, thereby cooling the body (see EVAPORATION). The sweat glands continuously release small amounts of sweat, but this is not noticeable because the sweat instantly evaporates. If the body temperature rises, however, messages are sent from the brain to the skin, causing the glands to pour out sweat. Hot weather, hard exercising, or a fever can all cause increased sweating, as can excitement or nervous tension. Many animals have no sweat glands. They lose moisture by evaporation from the mouth and lungs instead. This is why a dog pants when it is hot.

*See also* SKIN.

**SWEET GUM** The sweet gum tree is a deciduous tree that grows in the eastern United States (see DECIDUOUS TREE). It is a member of the witch hazel family (see WITCH HAZEL FAMILY). The sweet gum tree usually grows to a height of about 100 ft. [30 m]. It has star-shaped, lobed leaves that turn dark red in the fall (see LEAF). The flowers are either male or female and grow in stalked, ball-shaped clusters.

**SWEET GUM**
The sweet gum is easily recognized by its five-lobed leaves, which turn dark red in the fall.

Both types of flowers grow on the same plant (see MONOECIOUS).

The sweet gum produces a gummy substance that is used in perfumes and adhesives. The lumber is often used in fine furniture. The sweet gum tree is sometimes called the red gum.

**SWEET PEA**
Sweet peas are grown for their colorful, sweet-smelling flowers.

**SWEET PEA** The sweet pea is an annual plant that belongs to the pea family (see ANNUAL PLANT; PEA FAMILY). In climbing varieties, the vinelike stem is usually about 6 ft. [1.8 m] long. The compound leaves end in twining tendrils (see CLIMBING PLANT; TENDRIL). The flowers are red, pink, white, blue, or purple. They grow singly or in clusters. Seeds grow in hairy legumes, or pods, that are about 2 in. [5 cm] long (see LEGUME). There are more than one thousand cultivated varieties of sweet pea, most of which are very sweetly scented.

**SWEET POTATO** The sweet potato is a low-growing plant that belongs to the morning-glory family (see MORNING-GLORY). It is grown in tropical and subtropical areas for its edible, swollen roots. The stems of the sweet potato plant are long and creeping. The leaves vary in shape. Flowers grow in clusters in the axils of the leaves—that is, where the leaves meet the stems. The root of the sweet potato is eaten as a cooked vegetable or used as a pie filling. The sweet potato is not related to the potato or the yam.

**SWIFT** A swift is a bird that belongs to the family Apodidae. It has long, pointed wings; a short tail; a small bill; and tiny feet. A swift looks very similar to a swallow and flies through the air catching insects as a swallow does (see SWALLOW). It is faster than the swallow, however, and glides in the air for long periods of time. It actually spends more time in the air than any other bird and comes to earth only when nesting. It even sleeps in the air.

There are four species of swifts in North America. They range in length from 4 to 7 in. [11 to 18 cm]. All species are mostly black. However, the white-throated swift has a white patch on its throat and belly. Three of the four species are found only in western North America, but the chimney swift is found east of the Mississippi River. It is called a chimney swift because it roosts inside chimneys during the night. Chimney swifts can be seen in the summer over many eastern towns and cities.

**SWIM BLADDER** The swim bladder—more properly called the gas bladder—is a saclike organ found in many fish. It is usually located in the middle of the fish's body. Scientists believe the swim bladder in ancient fish evolved into the first lungs, giving rise to the amphibians (see AMPHIBIAN; EVOLUTION; LUNG). Some living fish, such as the lungfish, can absorb oxygen through their lunglike swim bladders (see LUNGFISH). Besides being used for breathing in some fish, the swim bladder is used to produce and detect sounds, and to change the buoyancy of the fish. This allows the fish to remain at a particular depth without floating up or sinking and to swim more easily.

*See also* BUOYANCY; FISH.

**SWIFT—Diving**
A swift has long, pointed wings which it folds close to its body as it swoops downward to catch insects (left).

**SWIFT—Variety**
Swifts are found throughout most of the world except northern Canada and Australia. Shown here are an African palm swift (right) and an Alpine swift from Europe (far right).

**SWITCH** A switch is a device that controls the flow of electricity in a circuit. Switches are used for such things as turning on and off lighting and heating equipment and electronic devices, such as televisions (see CIRCUIT, ELECTRIC; CURRENT, ELECTRIC; ELECTRICITY).

A switch works by completing or breaking a circuit. When the switch completes the circuit, an electric current flows, and the device is turned on. When the switch breaks the circuit, the electric current cannot flow, and the device is turned off. A switch often includes a lever that can be set at either "on" or "off." When the lever is in the "on" position, a metal bar presses against two metal contacts that are separated by an air space. The two contacts form part of the circuit. The bar conducts electricity. When the bar presses against the contacts, a current flows from one contact to the other through the bar. When the lever is in the "off" position, the bar does not touch the contacts. Therefore, no electricity flows in the circuit. The outer parts of the switch, including the lever, must be well insulated to keep electricity from flowing through them. Certain plastics are good insulators and are often used in switches (see INSULATION).

There are many different kinds of switches. In addition to switches that have levers, there are switches that operate by pressing a button, pulling a cord, or making a sound, such as talking or clapping hands. A kind of switch called a microswitch is operated by very small amounts of pressure or movement. A microswitch is often used to control electric wheelchairs. Some switches operate automatically. For example, certain switches can be made to turn on when sunlight falls below a certain strength (see PHOTOELECTRIC EFFECT). A thermostat is a kind of switch that operates automatically by the temperature of a substance (see THERMOSTAT). Still other switches are operated by vacuum or by electric current passing through a gas (see VACUUM).

A new kind of switch is called an electron switch. An electron switch operates by deflecting electron beams that are given off by an electron gun (see ELECTRON). The beams are deflected toward targets, activating a device. Electron switches eliminate the use of wires. In addition, the paths of the electrons can be much more specific when they are deflected instead of being carried by wires. Electron switches allow prostheses, such as artificial hands, to carry out very specific or tiny movements. *See also* ELECTRONICS; PROSTHETICS.

**SWORDFISH** A swordfish is a saltwater fish that belongs to the family Xiphiidae. It is called a swordfish because its upper jaw projects forward like a sword. The "sword" is believed to be used to stun small fish that the swordfish eats. Swordfish may reach a length of 12 ft. [3.6 m] or more.

The swordfish is found in both the Atlantic and Pacific oceans. It is a very fast swimmer, sometimes traveling at 60 m.p.h. [96 kph]. For this reason, it is a popular game fish. Swordfish is also a favorite seafood.

**SWORDFISH**

The swordfish is a saltwater fish found in both the Atlantic and the Pacific oceans. It is called a swordfish because of its upper jaw, which is in the shape of a sword.

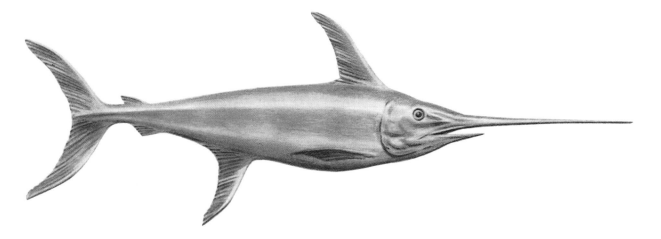

**SYCAMORE** (sĭk′ə môr′) The sycamores are a group of large, deciduous trees that belong to genus *Platanus* of the plane family (see DECIDUOUS TREE). They grow throughout the United States and often reach a height of 180 ft. [55 m]. The leaves are large, flat, and lobed (see LEAF). The flowers are either staminate (male) or pistillate (female) and grow in separate clusters on the same tree (see MONOECIOUS). The fruits hang in round balls on drooping stems. Sycamores are commonly planted along city streets.

**SYMBIOSIS** (sĭm′bē ō′sĭs) In general, symbiosis is the relationship between any two different organisms that are living together. This relationship may benefit, harm, or have no effect on one or both organisms. The word *symbiont* refers to an organism living in symbiosis, especially the smaller of the two organisms. There are three types of symbiosis: parasitism, commensalism, and mutualism.

In parasitism, one organism, the parasite, harms the other organism, the host (see PARASITE). The parasite gets nutrients and, in most cases, shelter from the host. An example of parasitism is the tapeworm found in the intestines of host animals (see TAPEWORM).

In commensalism, one organism benefits, and the other is usually unaffected (see COMMENSALISM). For example, the remora is a fish that attaches itself to a shark or other large fish. The remora feeds on small fish and leftovers from the shark's meals (see REMORA).

Mutualism is a relationship in which both organisms benefit. Lichens, for example, are fungi and algae living together (see LICHEN). The fungi get food from the photosynthetic algae. The algae get shelter and protection from the fungi. The terms *mutualism* and *symbiosis* are often used interchangeably.

**SYMMETRY** (sĭm'ĭ trē) *Symmetry* refers to equal or balanced proportions. Symmetry involves a balanced form or arrangement on opposite sides of a line or around an axis. For example, if some ink is splashed onto a sheet of paper and the paper is folded in half and the two sides are pressed together, a symmetrical pattern may be formed. The fold is called the line of symmetry. This means that the patterns on either side of the line are the same.

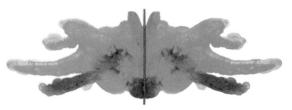

Geometrical shapes can be classified by their symmetry. An isosceles triangle is a triangle with only one line of symmetry. An equilateral triangle has three.

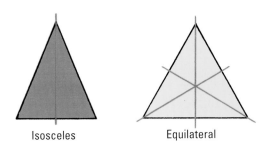

Isosceles          Equilateral

A quadrilateral (four-sided figure) with two lines of symmetry may be a rhombus or a rectangle. A quadrilateral with four lines of symmetry is a square.

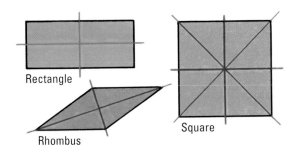

Rectangle

Rhombus

Square

If any shape is rotated through 360°, it then fits onto its own outline. However, a rectangle fits onto itself if it is rotated through 180°. This is called rotational symmetry of order 2.

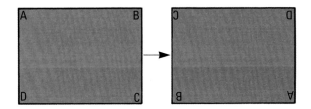

A square has rotational symmetry of order 4. It can be rotated through 90°, 180°, 270°, and 360°, and in each case fits into itself.

A solid object can have planes of symmetry and axes of symmetry. A plane of symmetry is one that cuts the object into symmetrical halves. An axis of symmetry is a line about which the object can be rotated and fit on its own outline. For example, a pyramid has one axis and four planes of symmetry. To make things simple, the diagram below shows only two planes. The other two planes pass through the corners of the pyramid.
*See also* GEOMETRY.

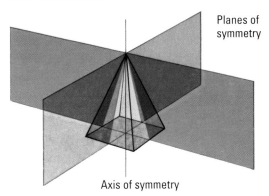

Planes of symmetry

Axis of symmetry

**SYNAPSE** (sĭn'ăps') A synapse is the tiny gap between two nerve cells (see NERVE CELL). There are billions of synapses in the nervous system. They act like switches, delivering nerve impulses along nerves. When a nerve impulse reaches a synapse, it causes the ending of the first nerve cell to release a chemical called a transmitter. This chemical passes across the gap and triggers the next nerve cell. There are a number of different transmitter substances found in different parts of the nervous system. Certain diseases, such as Parkinson's disease, result from a disorder in transmission between certain brain cells. Certain drugs also interfere with the amounts of transmitter substances that cross the synapses, as do some insecticides.
*See also* NERVOUS SYSTEM; PARKINSON'S DISEASE.

**SYNCLINE** (sĭn′klīn′) *Syncline* is a term in geology that refers to a downward fold or warp in layers of rock. The most recently formed rocks in a syncline occur at the axis, or center, of the syncline. A synclinorium is a downward fold made up of numerous minor folds.

*See also* FOLDING.

**SYNFUEL** Synfuel is synthetic fuel that can be used in place of natural gas and crude oil (see FUEL; NATURAL GAS; OIL). Synfuels are made from coal, bituminous sands, oil shale, and biomass (any type of organic matter) (see BIOMASS; COAL; OIL SHALE). Coal heated with steam and oxygen produces carbon monoxide, hydrogen, and methane. This gas mixture is used in place of natural gas (see CARBON MONOXIDE; HYDROGEN; METHANE). Coal liquefied under great pressure and at high temperatures produces a liquid like crude oil. Oil shale is a kind of rock that contains organic substances. These release vapors when heated that condense into a liquid oil.

Bituminous sands, also known as tar sands, contain bitumin, a black substance used to produce liquid fuel. These sands are heated with water to release the bitumin. Gasohol is fuel made by mixing alcohol obtained from fermenting biomass (sugar cane waste or other plant material) with gasoline (see FERMENTATION; GASOLINE).

**SYNTHESIS** (sĭn′thĭ sĭs) In chemistry, *synthesis* refers to making a compound from elements or other compounds rather than obtaining the compound from natural sources (see COMPOUND; ELEMENT). Some compounds are made synthetically because it is easier to make them than to take the substance from the plant, animal, or mineral. Synthetic compounds also may have desirable properties that the same natural compounds do not. Synthetic rubber is an example (see RUBBER). *Synthesis* also refers to the making of compounds that do not occur in nature at all.

Synthetics include all plastics and such manufactured fibers as acrylic and nylon. Gems and various foods also can be made synthetically.

**SYNTHETIC FIBER** Synthetic fibers are fibers made from chemicals rather than from plants or animals (see FIBER). They are used in many types of products including tires, brushes, insulation, carpets, and clothing.

Most synthetic fibers, like many plastics, are made by a process called polymerization from chemicals found in petroleum (see PETROLEUM; POLYMERIZATION). The chemicals consist mainly of carbon and hydrogen. In polymerization, small molecules are made to link up to form long chains called polymers (see POLYMER). Nylon, for example, is a polymer

**SYNTHETIC FIBER**
A climber uncoils a rope that is thin but extremely strong because it is made from synthetic fibers.

that consists of a chain of a type of molecule called an amide.

In many applications, synthetic fibers are more useful than natural ones because they are stronger and last longer. Fiber producers can work with polymer chemists to develop new fibers that have properties specially suited to a particular use. They can also control the size, shape, surface texture, and strength of the fibers they make.

The common synthetic fiber, nylon, is a good example (see NYLON). Fine nylon fibers are used to make stockings while thicker glossy nylon threads are used in other types of clothing. Thick nylon fibers are used as reinforcements in vehicle tires.

## SYPHILIS (sĭf'ə lĭs) Syphilis is a sexually transmitted disease caused by the bacterium called *Treponema pallidum* (see BACTERIA; SEXUALLY TRANSMITTED DISEASE). Syphilis is usually spread by sexual contact. A pregnant woman with syphilis, however, can spread the disease to her unborn child. The baby may have birth defects, or he or she may show no sign of the disease for as long as several years.

If syphilis goes untreated, the disease passes through three stages. The first stage begins ten days to ten weeks after infection. There may be a painless sore called a chancre where the syphilis bacteria entered the body. The chancre may not even be noticed, especially in women, where the sore is often inside the vagina. The chancre goes away by itself, but the disease does not go away.

The second stage of syphilis begins four weeks to several months after infection. This stage may produce a rash, fever, and feeling of illness. In many people, however, there are no signs at all. Within a few weeks, the second stage ends, and the infected person may feel perfectly healthy. The disease, however, has just begun to cause damage.

The third stage appears several months or even years later. The bacteria spread all over the body and may damage the brain, spinal cord, heart valves, and blood vessels. The disease may cause insanity, blindness, paralysis, or death.

Although syphilis is a very dangerous disease, it can be cured easily, particularly in the early stages.

Doctors use penicillin or other antibiotics to kill the disease-causing bacteria (see ANTIBIOTIC). It is important to note that syphilis, like other sexually transmitted diseases, does not go away by itself. It must be treated by a doctor. As with other sexually transmitted diseases, a person does not develop an immunity to syphilis (see IMMUNITY). Each time a person is infected, he or she must be treated with antibiotics.

*See also* REPRODUCTIVE SYSTEM.

## SYRINGE (sə rĭnj') A syringe is a device for injecting fluids or removing them by suction. Syringes are often used to inject drugs or vaccines into people or animals or for taking samples of blood or other fluids from the body for testing.

A syringe is made up of a hollow barrel, a plunger or soft hollow bulb, and a hollow needle. The plunger or hollow bulb is used either to create suction or to force fluid from the syringe. In the past, most syringes were made of glass and had to be very carefully sterilized to make sure that they did not transfer infections or germs. Now, most syringes are disposable. They are used only once before they are thrown away.

# T

## TALC (tălk) Talc, the softest of all minerals, is usually found in metamorphic rocks (see METAMORPHIC ROCK; MINERAL). Compact masses of talc are called soapstone. Talc ranges in color from white to dark gray.

Talc has many uses. Its best-known use may be as a body powder, called talcum powder. Tailors (people who make and mend clothes) use talc to mark clothes. Talc is used in the manufacture of crayons, paint, pottery, and other products. Because talc is heat resistant, slabs of it are used to line furnaces and heating stoves.

The United States produces a great deal of talc. Most of it comes from New York, California, and North Carolina.

**TANAGER** (tăn′ĭ jər) Tanagers are colorful birds that belong to the family Thraupidae. There are about 250 species, ranging up to about 8 in. [20 cm] in length. Tanagers live in forests, where they feed on fruits and insects. A few species of tanagers live in North America. The scarlet, summer, and western tanagers are the most common of these species. The male scarlet tanager has a red body and black wings and tail. The male summer tanager is all red. The male western tanager has a yellow body, red head, and black tail and wings.
*See also* BIRD.

**TANAGER**

Tanagers are colorful birds that live mainly in the warm parts of the Americas. Pictured is a rose-breasted thrush tanager.

**TANNING** Tanning is a process used in the changing of animal hide (skin) into leather. Many experts believe that tanning is the oldest industry in the world. Although the methods of tanning have changed, the basic principles have stayed the same. The factory where tanning occurs is called a tannery.

The first step in preparing a hide for tanning is to thoroughly wash the hide, which has been removed from the animal. The hide is then often cured by covering it with sodium chloride (salt) to help it dry. In warm climates, the hide is sometimes dried by air. Drying helps prevent the hide from decomposing (see DECOMPOSITION).

The hide is then placed in a large turning vat (drum), which contains a solution of water, lime, and a small amount of sodium sulfide. This solution causes the hair roots on the hide to weaken, so that the hair can be easily scraped away. This is known as unhairing.

Tanning can be done using one of three main methods—vegetable, mineral, or a combination of the two. Vegetable tanning involves placing the hide in a series of solutions. These solutions contain water and tannin, a substance obtained from certain plants. The tannin combines with the protein in the hide to produce a compound that does not decompose easily (see COMPOUND; PROTEIN). This compound is called leather. The vegetable tanning process may take from a few hours to several months, depending on the kind of hide and its future use. Vegetable tanning is often used to produce tough leather for book covers and machinery belts.

Mineral tanning, also known as chrome tanning, often involves pickling, or placing the hides that have been treated with lime in a solution of acid and salt (see ACIDS; SALTS). The hides are then tumbled in large turning vats that usually hold solutions of chromium compounds. Tanning with chromium compounds began at the end of the 1800s. It helped shorten the process of tanning from weeks to days. Mineral tanning is often used to produce soft leather.

Combination tanning often involves mineral tanning followed by vegetable tanning. This speeds the vegetable tanning process and makes vegetable-tanned leather less stiff.

**TANNING**

At this tannery in Morocco, recently tanned hides hang in the sun to dry before being dyed in one of the vats.

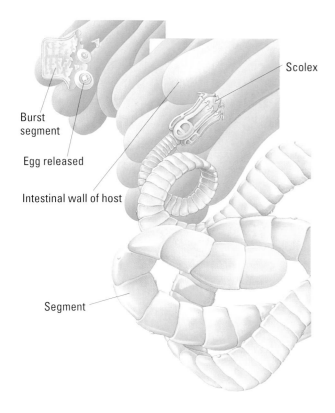

**TAPEWORM**

A tapeworm attaches itself to its host's intestinal wall using hooks on its head (called a scolex). Eggs are released when body segments break free and burst open.

Labels: Burst segment, Egg released, Intestinal wall of host, Segment, Scolex

**TAPEWORM** A tapeworm is an internal parasite that lives in the intestines of human beings and other animals (see INTESTINE; PARASITE). The tapeworm belongs to a group of animals called flatworms. A tapeworm has a slender, flattened body made up of segments (pieces). Some tapeworms are less than 1 in. [2.5 cm] long and have only three or four segments. Others can be 30 ft. [9 m] long with thousands of segments.

The head of a tapeworm, called the scolex, attaches itself to the wall of the animal's intestine with a set of hooks and suckers. The animal it attaches to is called the host. As the tapeworm grows, new segments are produced just behind the scolex. Older segments gradually move farther back. The tapeworm has no mouth. It is surrounded by food already digested by the host and simply absorbs this food through its body wall.

Tapeworms produce millions of eggs in their body segments. The older segments gradually break free and pass out of the host with the feces. Humans may become infected by eating foods that contain tapeworm eggs, but most infections arise from eating undercooked meat, especially pork and beef. This is because the early stages in the life history of "human" tapeworms are passed in the muscles of pigs and cattle. Anyone who thinks he or she may be infected should be examined and treated by a physician.

*See also* PLATYHELMINTHES; WORM.

**TAPIR** (tā'pər) Tapir is the name for a heavy, hoofed mammal related to the horse and rhinoceros (see MAMMAL). The tapir looks like a young rhinoceros. Its nose is drawn out, forming a short trunk. Each front foot has four toes. Each hind foot has three. Most tapirs live in tropical rain forests (see RAIN FOREST). They spend much of their time in the water. Tapirs feed on a wide range of terrestrial and aquatic plants. Two kinds of tapirs live in South America. One kind lives in forest regions east of the Andes mountains. Another makes its home high in the Andes mountains. The smallest species of the tapir family (Baird's tapir) lives in Mexico.

**TAPIR**

Baird's tapir (top), shown with its striped baby, lives in Mexico. Like the Brazilian tapir (bottom), it has a mane of bristles on its neck.

The Malayan tapir, found in southeast Asia, is larger than the American tapir. It is up to 8 ft. [2.4 m] long and stands about 3 ft. [91 cm] at the shoulder. This tapir has unusual coloring. The head, shoulders, and legs are black. The rest of the body is white. This makes the animal hard to see when it is in its natural surroundings (see CAMOUFLAGE).

Tapirs are sometimes hunted for their flesh and hides. Because of the hunting and the cutting down of forests, tapirs are becoming rare in some areas.

**TARANTULA** (tə răn′chə lə) The tarantulas are a group of large, hairy spiders (see SPIDER). They are hunters and do not make webs. In Europe, the name *tarantula* is often given to a large wolf spider. At one time, people thought a bite from this spider caused a disease called tarantism. Many believed this disease could only be cured by wild dancing. Scientists later discovered that most tarantulas are not harmful to human beings.

**TARANTULA**

The tarantula is a large, hairy spider. Tarantulas are found in the southern and western regions of the United States.

One of the largest spiders is the tarantula known as the bird spider of South America. Its legs can span 10 in. [24 cm]. The bird spider lives in trees and feeds on young birds. In the United States, most tarantulas are found in the south and west. Female tarantulas may live for more than twenty years.

**TARPON** (tär′pən) A tarpon is a saltwater fish that belongs to the family Elopidae (see FISH). The tarpon is sometimes also found in fresh water. The tarpon is a silvery fish with an upturned mouth and a long filament (thread) attached to the fin on its back. The fish may reach a length of 8 ft. [2.4 m] and may weigh 300 lb. [131 kg].

The tarpon is a popular game fish in North America. It is found in the warm parts of the Atlantic Ocean, around Florida, and in the Caribbean Sea.

**TARSAL** (tär′səl) The tarsals are bones that form the heel and the back part of the instep of the foot. There are seven tarsal bones: calcaneus, cuboid,

talus, navicular, and the three cuneiform bones. There are nineteen other bones in the foot. They are the five metatarsals (middle bones) and fourteen phalanges (toe bones).

*See also* BONE; PHALANGES.

**TARSIER** (tär'sē ər) Tarsiers are small primates that live in Indonesia and the Philippines (see PRIMATE). They have long hind legs, small round faces, and huge eyes and ears. The tarsier's body is about 6 in. [15 cm] long and is covered with thick brownish gray fur. Its tail is about twice as long as its body. These primates live in trees, usually feeding on insects and other small animals. They are nocturnal, feeding and hopping through the trees at night (see NOCTURNAL BEHAVIOR). Their fingers and toes have small, suckerlike pads, which help them climb.

**TARTAR** (tär'tər) Tartar, also called calculus, is a hard, yellowish substance that may be deposited on the teeth. Tartar is formed by the buildup of plaque. Plaque is a sticky film that is always forming on the teeth. Plaque can be removed by daily flossing and brushing. Tartar can be removed by a dentist or dental hygienist. If not properly removed, plaque and calculus irritate the gums. The irritation makes the gum tissue become inflamed (see INFLAMMATION). The gums may then recede, and the bone under the gum can become infected (see INFECTION). This condition will lead to a loosening of the teeth in the jawbone. In severe cases, teeth will fall out.

*See also* CARIES; DENTISTRY; TEETH.

**TARTARIC ACID** (tär tăr'ĭk ăs'ĭd) Tartaric acid ($C_4H_6O_6$) is a white organic (carbon-containing) compound (see COMPOUND). Tartaric acid is used in making jelly and soft drinks. It is a weak acid and forms salts called tartrates (see ACID; SALTS). Sodium potassium tartrate is an example of such a salt, which is known as Rochelle salt. Rochelle salt is used to make baking powder and mirrors.

**TASMANIAN DEVIL** (tăz mā'nē ən dĕv'əl) The Tasmanian devil is a stocky, doglike marsupial that lives only in remote areas of Tasmania, a large island off the south coast of Australia (see MARSUPIAL). The Tasmanian devil grows to a length of about 30 in. [75 cm], including its tail, which is about 10 in. [25 cm] long. Its fur is brownish black with white markings. The Tasmanian devil is nocturnal, moving about at night and sleeping in its burrow during the day (see NOCTURNAL BEHAVIOR).

The Tasmanian devil is a meat eater and eats a wide range of other animals. It is especially fond of carrion (dead and decaying bodies). It has large teeth and powerful jaws and often attacks animals much bigger than itself.

Like other marsupials, the Tasmanian devil has a pouch. After a gestation period of about a month, the female gives birth to three or four young. The young live in the pouch for four or five months.

*See also* GESTATION PERIOD.

**TASMANIAN DEVIL**

The Tasmanian devil is a ferocious, doglike marsupial (pouched mammal) that often attacks animals much bigger than itself.

**TASMANIAN WOLF** (tăz mā'nē ən wŏŏlf) The Tasmanian wolf, or Tasmanian tiger, was a carnivorous marsupial of Tasmania, an island off the south coast of Australia (see CARNIVORE; MARSUPIAL). Most scientists believe the animal is now extinct, having been killed off by European settlers (see EXTINCTION). The Tasmanian wolf looked like a dog except for its tail, which was rather stiff. It was the size of a small wolf. The Tasmanian wolf had short, coarse hair. It was mainly brown in color with black stripes across its back.

# TASTE AND SMELL

Taste and smell are the senses that respond to chemicals in the environment (see SENSE). Many simple animals have a single sense that detects chemicals through their moist body surface. Air-breathing vertebrates (animals with backbones), however, have separate receptors for taste and for smell (see RECEPTOR).

Taste, or gustation, is the detection and identification of dissolved chemicals that come in contact with the animal. Among the invertebrates (animals without backbones), insects seem to have the most highly developed sense of taste (see INSECT). They may have contact chemoreceptors (organs for taste) on their feet, antennae, mouthparts, or ovipositor (egg-laying tube). Among the vertebrates, there are many different types of contact chemoreceptors. For example, a fish can taste with its fins and tail as well as with its mouth. In most mammals, including humans, contact chemoreceptors are concentrated in the mouth, mostly on the tongue. The tongue is a muscular structure that is covered with a moist mucous membrane (see MAMMAL; MUCOUS MEMBRANE).

If the surface of the tongue were dry, there would be no sense of taste because there would be no moisture to dissolve the chemicals. The tongue has many small bumps called papillae. These papillae contain groups of contact chemoreceptors called taste buds. Taste buds stimulate nearby nerve cells that lead to the brain (see BRAIN; NERVE CELL).

Traditionally, tastes have been divided into four groups: salty, sweet, bitter, and acid (sour). Certain parts of the tongue are more sensitive than others to these specific tastes. Salty and sweet chemicals are more easily tasted by the tip of the tongue, bitter by the base of the tongue, and acid by the sides of the tongue. Some chemicals, however, are tasted by the entire surface of the tongue. The taste buds, like skin cells, are constantly being replaced. About half of the taste buds are replaced every ten days (see SKIN).

The flavor of food is only partially determined by the sense of taste. Other factors, such as the temperature, moistness, texture, and smell of the food, affect its flavor. This is the reason that someone with a cold—and therefore, nasal congestion—may find that many foods taste the same. It is also the reason that many foods do not taste the same if they are chopped into small bits.

Smell, or olfaction, is the detection and identification of chemicals in the air. For this reason, smell is sometimes called distance chemoreception. Distance chemoreceptors, or olfactory receptors,

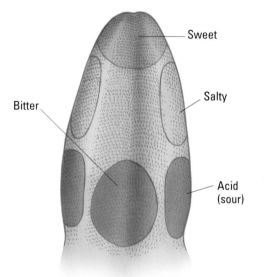

Sweet

Salty

Bitter

Acid (sour)

**SENSE RECEPTORS**

The receptors for the sense of taste are located on the surface of the tongue (above). Different areas detect sweet, salty, bitter, and acid (sour) flavors. Scent receptors are located in the roof of the nasal cavity (right).

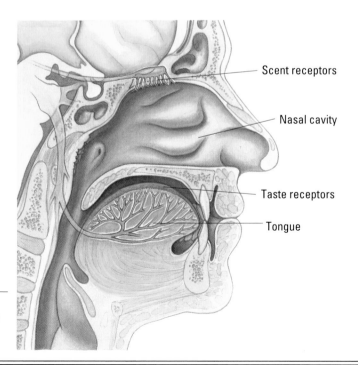

Scent receptors

Nasal cavity

Taste receptors

Tongue

are located in the moist mucous membranes of the nasal cavity in most animals (see NOSE). Some animals, such as lizards and snakes, have a special odor-sensitive organ in the mouth or in the septum, the partition between the nostrils.

For many animals, the sense of smell is the most important sense. It helps them detect enemies and locate food and mates. Although the sense of smell is less highly developed in humans than in many other animals, it is at least ten thousand times more sensitive than the sense of taste. In fact, most people can detect the odor of less than one trillionth of a gram of certain chemicals in a liter (about a quart) of air. One trillionth is one million-millionth, or 0.000000000001 g [0.0000000000003 oz]. Most people's nasal cavities have about 25.8 million olfactory receptors per sq. in. [40,000 per sq. mm]. Most other land mammals have many more. The rabbit, for example, has about 77.4 million receptors per sq. in. [120,000 receptors per sq. mm].

Animals also use their sense of smell for communication. Special chemicals called pheromones are detected by olfactory receptors (see PHEROMONE). Pheromones influence many types of behavior, including mating. For example, if a male monkey has its nose blocked, it will not respond to a female monkey who is in heat (ready to mate). Once its

nose is unblocked, however, the monkey detects the female's pheromones and mates with her. Recent studies have shown other interesting aspects of the sense of smell. For instance, a recently mated female animal was exposed to the odor of a strange male. This blocked normal hormonal changes in the female, and the fertilized egg in her body did not develop (see HORMONE; PREGNANCY).

Although an odor may at first be very strong, within a short time it seems to disappear. This is because the olfactory receptors adapt to, or become used to, the odor. As a result, they stop sending signals to the brain, and the person is no longer aware of the odor. Another person entering the area, however, will notice the odor instantly. This person soon adapts to the odor. If the odor becomes stronger, the olfactory receptors again send messages to the brain. After a while, the receptors adapt to this higher level, and the person is no longer aware of the odor. The level needed to stimulate the olfactory receptors is called the threshold. Adaptation to an odor is simply a raising of this threshold. **PROJECT 63, 74**

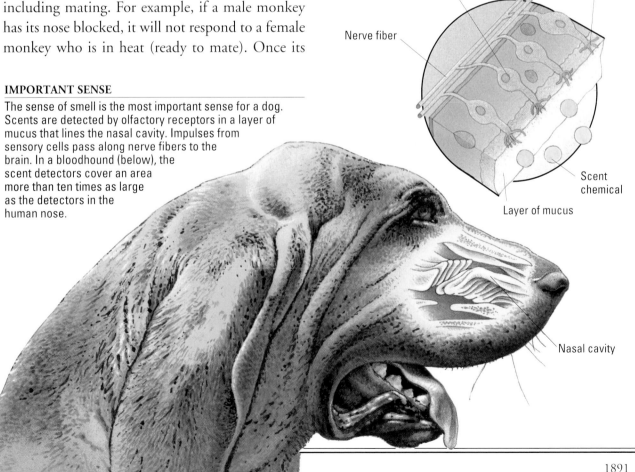

Sensory cell

Olfactory receptor

Nerve fiber

Scent chemical

Layer of mucus

Nasal cavity

**IMPORTANT SENSE**

The sense of smell is the most important sense for a dog. Scents are detected by olfactory receptors in a layer of mucus that lines the nasal cavity. Impulses from sensory cells pass along nerve fibers to the brain. In a bloodhound (below), the scent detectors cover an area more than ten times as large as the detectors in the human nose.

**TAXIDERMY** (tăk´sĭ dûr´mē) Taxidermy is the practice of preparing animal skins and stuffing them so they can be displayed in a lifelike manner. The word *taxidermy* comes from two Greek words meaning "arrangement" and "skin." Museums of natural history often show animals, birds, and fish in this way. Fishers and hunters sometimes have prize catches or kills stuffed and mounted for display.

Taxidermists, the people who practice taxidermy, study the habits and movements of wildlife so that they are better able to present them in a natural state. The process of taxidermy first involves taking measurements of the dead animal. The skin is carefully removed and treated with a preservative, so it will not rot. Next, the taxidermist makes a model of the animal's body using a wire frame and clay, paper, plaster, or wood. The skin is sewn onto the model. Skins of large animals are usually tanned before being mounted on the model.
*See also* TANNING.

**TAXONOMY** (tăk sŏn´ə mē) Taxonomy is the science that identifies, names, and classifies organisms. The organisms may be living now or may have lived in the past. The current taxonomic system has seven main divisions: kingdom, phylum (often called *division* in kingdoms other than the animal kingdom), class, order, family, genus, and species.
*See also* CLASSIFICATION OF LIVING ORGANISMS.

**TEA** Tea is one of the most popular drinks in the world. It is made from the leaves of the tea plant. Tea plants have long, pointed leaves and small, sweet-smelling, white flowers. Each flower produces three seeds. In places where tea is grown commercially (for sale), the seeds are removed and planted in a nursery bed. In about one year, when the plants have reached a height of 8 in. [20 cm], they are transplanted to a field. Wild tea plants grow as high as 30 ft. [9 m]. Commercial tea plants are pruned (cut) to keep them about 3 to 4 ft. [1 to 1.2 m] in height so that the leaves can be picked easily. The tea plant is grown commercially chiefly in China, India, Japan, Sri Lanka, Russia, Turkey, and several African and South American countries. About 3 billion lb. [1.4 billion kg] of tea are produced each year.

There are three main kinds of tea—black tea, green tea, and oolong tea. They differ in the methods used to prepare the leaves. To make black tea, the leaves are first spread on shelves. Air is blown over the leaves to remove most of the moisture. The leaves are crushed between rollers to squeeze out the juices. In the fermenting room, the leaves change chemically under controlled humidity and

**TEA—Growing**
Tea is a major cash crop in many parts of Asia. This carefully tended tea plantation is in the highlands of Malaysia.

**TEA—Harvesting**

The best tea is made from young, green leaves from the top of the plant. This worker is gathering tea in Sri Lanka, one of the world's major producers of tea.

temperature, turning copper in color (see FERMENTATION). The leaves are then dried further in ovens, where they turn brownish black. Green tea is made by steaming the leaves in large vats (drums). The leaves are then crushed and dried. Oolong tea is made by partly fermenting the leaves. Oolong tea is usually greenish brown in color.

Tea is brewed by pouring boiling water over (usually) one teaspoon of loose tea, or one tea bag, per cup. In the United States, iced tea is the most popular form of this beverage.

**TEAK** (tēk) Teak is a tree found in southern Asia. The teak tree grows to a height of 150 ft. [46 m]. Its leaves are often 2 ft. [61 cm] in length. They yield a purple dye. The leaves are used for wrapping material and for roofs.

The wood from a teak tree is strong and resists water. The wood also contains an oil that helps it resist insects such as termites. Teakwood takes a high polish. It is greatly valued for parts of ships and for furniture. India, Myanmar (formerly Burma), and Thailand produce teakwood for sale to other countries. A tree called African teak is also valued for its wood. African teak belongs to the spurge family. True teak belongs to the vervain family. *See also* SPURGE FAMILY; TREE.

**TEAK**

Teak is used for making furniture and paneling. It is often decorated with intricate designs by skilled wood carvers, as here in Thailand.

# TECHNOLOGY

Technology (těk nŏl′ə jē) is all the means by which a society produces goods, using energy, materials, tools, and methods. The goods are used to satisfy needs and wants.

Early people were using technology when they made and used simple tools and built fires. Often, people used a particular kind of technology before they understood the science behind how the technology worked. For example, the method of combining the metals copper and zinc to form the alloy brass has been in use since about 500 B.C. (see ALLOY; METAL AND METALLURGY). However, people did not understand exactly how or why the metals combined until after the idea of the atom was developed in the 1800s (see ATOM; CHEMISTRY). In other cases, advances have only been possible because scientists have made new discoveries about the laws of chemistry and physics (see PHYSICS). Scientists have applied such knowledge to produce different inventions (see INVENTION). These inventions in turn have been used in producing goods. Today, sophisticated machines are used to produce goods on a large scale. These machines are powered using various forms of energy, such as burning fossil fuels (see ENERGY).

The level of modern technology has led to some problems. For example, scientists have been able to make materials that are not found in nature, such as plastics. When these materials are finished being used and are disposed of, they are not easily broken down by the forces of nature. They remain as pollution (see POLLUTION; WASTE DISPOSAL). Also, the amount of materials and energy required to make goods on a large scale has led to problems. For example, certain natural resources, such as fossil fuels, trees, and land, are being depleted (see FOSSIL FUEL; NATURAL RESOURCE). In addition, the widespread use of fossil fuels has released pollution into the atmosphere. Today, scientists are developing technology to try to solve these problems.

**MODERN TECHNOLOGY**
Products of modern technology include personal computers (above) and robots (left). Personal computers have given computing power to individuals in homes, schools, and offices. Robots have revolutionized assembly processes in industries such as automobile manufacturing.

Teeth are hard, bonelike structures found in the mouths of most vertebrates (animals with backbones). Some animals use their teeth as weapons. Most animals use their teeth to seize, tear, and chew food. Humans also use their teeth to help form certain sounds when speaking.

All true vertebrate teeth evolved from the bony plates that covered some of the prehistoric fishes (see EVOLUTION). The shape, size, and number of teeth in an animal partly depends on its behavior and diet. Each species, however, has a certain tooth pattern. This fact is often used in identifying animal remains or fossils (see FOSSIL). By comparing the teeth of different living and extinct animals, scientists are able to tell from which animal another animal evolved (see EXTINCTION).

**Parts of a tooth** In general, teeth have two main parts: the crown and the root. The crown is the white part of the tooth that can be seen. The root is below the part of the mouth called the gum. Each

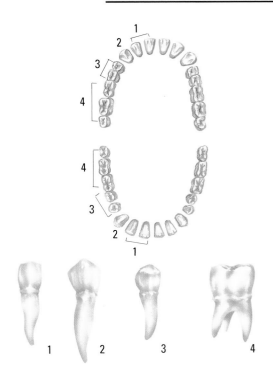

**TYPES OF TEETH**

Counting the teeth in both upper and lower jaws, an adult human being has (1) eight incisors, (2) four canines, (3) eight bicuspids, and (4) twelve molars. There are thirty-two teeth in all. A child has only twenty teeth, known as primary teeth.

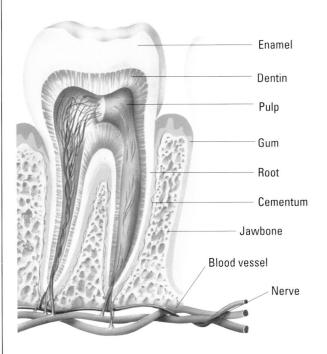

**STRUCTURE OF A TOOTH**

In this section of a molar tooth, a hard enamel covers the softer dentin, which surrounds the pulp cavity containing nerves and blood vessels. Below gum level, cementum holds the root firmly to the jawbone.

Enamel

Dentin

Pulp

Gum

Root

Cementum

Jawbone

Blood vessel

Nerve

root usually has a special socket, or space, in the jaw. The part of the tooth at the gum line, where the crown and the root meet, is called the neck.

All true teeth are made up of three layers. In mammals, the outer layer of the crown is called enamel (see MAMMAL). Enamel is the hardest substance in the body. It is tougher and stronger than bone. Inside the enamel layer is dentin. Dentin is similar to bone and not as hard as enamel (see BONE). It makes up most of the tooth. The innermost layer is pulp. Pulp contains many tiny blood vessels and a nerve (see NERVOUS SYSTEM). The dentin is nourished by the pulp. The nerve and blood vessels enter the pulp through a passage in the root called the root canal. The root itself is covered by a layer of tough material called cementum.

In most vertebrates other than mammals, the outer layer is called vitrodentin. Vitrodentin is a form of dentin that is almost as hard as enamel. Many of these animals have teeth that lack roots and cementum.

**Human teeth** Humans have two sets of teeth during their lifetime—primary teeth and permanent teeth. Primary teeth are also called deciduous, milk, or baby teeth. They begin to break through the gums when a baby is about six months old. All twenty primary teeth usually are in place by the time the child is three years old. The permanent teeth begin forcing out and taking the place of primary teeth when the child is about six years old. All thirty-two permanent teeth usually are in place by the time the person is in his or her early twenties.

The thirty-two permanent teeth are arranged in pairs on each side of the upper and lower jaws. There are four types of permanent teeth: incisors, canines, bicuspids, and molars. The incisors are the eight front teeth, four in each jaw. They have sharp edges and are used for cutting and holding food. The canines are four pointed teeth, one on each side of the incisors, two in each jaw. These strong teeth are used for tearing food. The canines are sometimes called eyeteeth or cuspids. Each of the incisors and canines has a single root.

Next to each canine are two bicuspids, four in each jaw. The bicuspids are also called premolars. Each bicuspid has two cusps (peaks) and one or two roots. Behind each pair of bicuspids are three molars, six in each jaw. The molars have several cusps and roots. The third molars are sometimes called wisdom teeth because they usually appear when the person is a teenager. The bicuspids and molars are used for chewing and crushing food.

**The teeth of other vertebrates** In crocodiles, some fish, and most mammals, the teeth are held in bony sockets by what is called a periodontal membrane. This membrane acts like a shock absorber. In some fish, amphibians, and reptiles, the teeth are attached directly to the jawbones. In other reptiles, the teeth are attached to a bony ridge that juts out from the jawbones. The teeth of sharks and rays are attached to the skin inside the mouth.

In many fish, amphibians, and reptiles, all the teeth are the same shape. When the teeth are worn down, they are shed and replaced. Most mammals and bony fishes have several different kinds of teeth, each of which has a special use. Most mammals

have two sets of teeth during their lifetimes. Some, however, have only one. Some vertebrates, such as modern birds, turtles, some anteaters, some bony fishes, and some whales, do not have any teeth. Prehistoric birds, however, did have teeth. Some amphibians, such as frogs, have teeth only in their upper jaws.

Many vertebrates have teeth that are specially adapted to their life-styles. Most poisonous snakes have hollow teeth called fangs. These fangs are used

**SHARP TEETH**

The gharial, a type of crocodile from northern India, has dozens of needle-sharp teeth for seizing the fish on which it feeds.

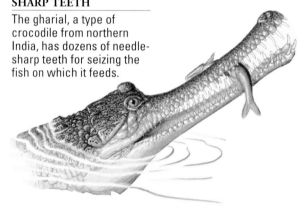

to inject poison into a victim (see SNAKE). The saw-fish has teeth outside its mouth, fixed to a bladelike beak. These teeth are used to slash prey. The tusks of an elephant are actually large incisors. The tusks of a walrus, on the other hand, are large canines. Both kinds of tusks are composed of a form of dentin called ivory (see IVORY). In general, carnivorous predators (meat-eating animals that hunt and kill other animals) have long, pointed canine teeth. These teeth are used to kill prey and to tear it apart.

Most herbivorous (plant-eating) animals have short, flat teeth. These teeth can bite and chew plant material. One group of herbivorous mammals, the ruminants, has no teeth in the front of the upper jaw. The lower teeth bite against a tough, horny pad.

*See also* DENTISTRY; RUMINANT.

### TUSKS
An elephant's tusks are actually large incisor teeth growing out of the upper jaw.

## TELECOMMUNICATION

**TELECOMMUNICATION** Telecommunication is the transmitting (sending) and receiving of information over long distances. Today, telecommunication is often carried out through the use of electronic devices. Telecommunication includes communication by radio, telephone, and television (see ELECTRONICS; RADIO; TELEPHONE; TELEVISION).

An early form of telecommunication was the telegraph, which was invented in 1837 (see TELEGRAPH). Telecommunication has exploded since then. It has become part of everyday life and has linked people all over the world. For example, telecommunication allows people to hear music or news that is being broadcast from a radio station that is miles away. Telecommunication allows a person in California to have a telephone conversation with a person in England. Telecommunication allows a scene that occurred in the Middle East to be viewed on televisions in the United States.

Many forms of modern telecommunication rely on an electronic procedure called modulation. Modulation involves the mixing of signals. For example, in order for the radio waves that represent sound to be transmitted, they must be combined with another kind of radio wave called a carrier wave. Only in this form can they be transmitted over long distances. An antenna receives the waves and converts them into the electric signals needed by the receiving electronic device, such as a radio.

*See also* ANTENNA.

**TELECOMMUNICATION**
The antennas on this tall telecommunications tower transmit signals, using microwave radio links, to other towers.

**TELEGRAPH** The telegraph was the first device to send messages by electricity along a wire (see ELECTRICITY). During the early days of the telegraph, in the 1800s, messages were tapped out in Morse code using a special key. Morse code is a system of dots (short electrical signals) and dashes (long electrical signals). Each letter of the alphabet and each punctuation mark is represented by a group of these signals (see MORSE CODE). The signals were sent out over a wire to an operator at the receiving end. The operator interpreted the dots and dashes and typed them on paper to form a message, called a telegram. The telegram was then hand delivered to the receiver. A person who wanted to send a telegram went to the office of the telegraph company, wrote out a message, handed it to the clerk, and paid for it.

Three men are given credit for the invention of the telegraph. In 1837, William F. Cooke and Charles Wheatstone of England introduced a telegraph that worked by electromagnetism (see ELECTROMAGNETISM). During that same year, Samuel Morse, an American inventor, successfully sent signals over a telegraph of his own design (see MORSE, SAMUEL FINLEY BREESE). Morse's signals traveled over a wire that was 1,700 ft. [518 m] long. Later, Morse developed the Morse code and a relay system that allowed messages to travel longer distances. Morse convinced the United States government to build a test telegraph line between Washington, D.C., and Baltimore, Maryland. On May 24, 1844, Morse, in Washington, tapped out a message that said, "What hath God wrought?" The operator in Baltimore received the message and sent it back to Washington.

The use of the telegraph spread rapidly throughout the 1800s. The United States became crisscrossed with telegraph wires. In 1861, a telegraph cable was laid along the bottom of the Atlantic Ocean. It connected the United States with Europe. Today, communicating by telegraph has largely been replaced by communicating through computer modem, facsimile (fax) machine, and telephone. In many countries a telegram service is no longer available.

*See also* COMPUTER; FACSIMILE MACHINE; TELEPHONE.

**TELEMETRY** (tə lĕm′ĭ trē) Telemetry is the process by which data (information) is sent to Earth from instruments that are far away. Telemetry is used to send data from weather balloons (radiosondes), artificial satellites, and space probes (see RADIOSONDE; SATELLITE; SPACE EXPLORATION).

A telemetry system is made up of several parts. A measuring device is used to gather the needed information. For example, in a radiosonde, a measuring device might be a thermometer. The data gathered by the measuring device is changed into radio signals and sent to Earth (see RADIO). The receiving station then translates the signals. Telemetry plays an important part in the United States space program. Information about space is sent from unmanned spacecraft back to Earth by telemetry systems. Telemetry systems also record the physical conditions of astronauts during manned space missions.

**TELEMETRY**

Telemetry is used to send data to Earth from remote instruments. In 1986, the *Giotto* space probe took close-up pictures of Halley's comet. Electronic equipment converted pictures taken by the camera into radio signals, which were beamed back to Earth.

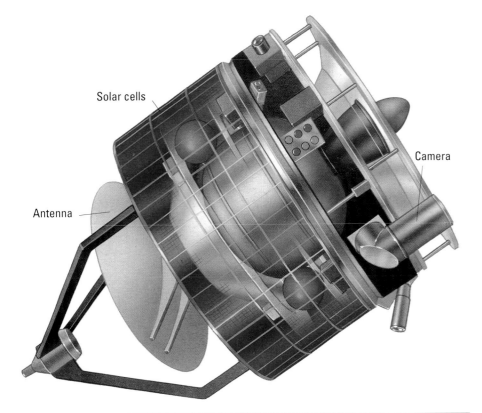

Solar cells

Camera

Antenna

# TELEPHONE

A telephone is a device generally used to transmit (send) and receive sound, especially voices. *Telephone* comes from the Greek words *tele*, meaning "far," and *phone*, meaning "sound." The telephone is one of the most important means of communication today.

**A brief history** In 1876, Alexander Graham Bell, a professor of speech at Boston University in Massachusetts, invented the telephone (see BELL, ALEXANDER GRAHAM). Bell had first experimented with sending several messages over a telegraph wire at the same time (see TELEGRAPH). He then learned how to send the vibrations of a musical tone over wire. He believed that a human voice could be sent over wire in much the same way. Bell and his assistant, Thomas Augustus Watson, began to work on an instrument to transmit the human voice. On March 10, 1876, Bell spoke the first complete sentence into his invention, the telephone, to Watson: "Mr. Watson, come here; I want you."

In Bell's device, sound waves from his voice set up vibrations in a thin disk called a diaphragm. Attached to the diaphragm was a rod made of magnetic material. The vibrating diaphragm caused the rod to move toward and away from an electromagnet (see ELECTROMAGNETISM; MAGNETISM). These movements caused an electric current to be produced in a metal coil. From the coil, the current traveled through a wire to the same kind of device on the other end, which now acted as a receiver (see CURRENT, ELECTRIC). The electric current caused the diaphragm at the listener's end to vibrate. As the diaphragm vibrated, it pulled and pushed air in front of it. This caused the air to form sound waves that were similar to the sound waves that were originally spoken.

Bell's first telephone produced such weak electric currents that it could not be used over long distances. Several important advancements made the telephone practical for communication over long distances. One of these advancements was made by

Mouthpiece cover    Diaphragm

Crystal microphone

**TELEPHONE PRINCIPLE**
The designs of telephones vary from country to country, but they all work on the same principle. This telephone has been given a case of transparent plastic to show the components inside. The part the user holds—called the handset—has a mouthpiece and an earpiece. The transmitter in the mouthpiece is usually a crystal microphone. The receiver in the earpiece is a miniature loudspeaker.

the American inventor Thomas Alva Edison in 1877 (see EDISON, THOMAS ALVA). Edison invented a separate transmitter (device for transmitting sounds). He still used Bell's invention as the receiver of sounds.

In Edison's transmitter, there were grains of carbon behind the diaphragm. Carbon is a good conductor of electricity (see CARBON; CONDUCTION OF ELECTRICITY). When sound waves caused the diaphragm to vibrate, the diaphragm pressed against the carbon. The louder the sound was, the more the diaphragm was forced to bend. This in turn caused the grains to become more tightly packed. The softer the sound, the less the diaphragm was forced to bend. This caused the grains to become less tightly packed. The electric current was supplied by a battery. The amount that the grains were packed affected the amount of electricity that was allowed to flow. Being tightly packed meant the grains conducted electricity better, producing a stronger electric current. Being less tightly packed meant the grains conducted less electricity. A weaker electric current was produced. Thus, the combination of the strong and weak currents formed signals that copied the original sound waves. These signals were sent over wires to the receiver and heard as sound.

Another advance occurred in 1877, when Thomas B. Doolittle suggested that copper be used to make wire instead of the iron that had been used. Electricity passes easily through copper, preventing loss in the power of transmitted speech.

As the telephone improved, the possibility of telephones becoming widespread became a reality. However, this presented another problem. Under the existing system, each telephone had to be connected by wires to every other telephone. This system became impractical as the number of telephones increased. Switching, or connecting, equipment located at a central office solved this problem. Each telephone was connected by wire to the central office. The signals from a transmitting telephone traveled to the central office. There, an operator, using a device called a switchboard, connected the signals to the receiving telephone. Automatic switching equipment came into use in the 1920s.

There have been several significant modern-day improvements in the telephone. In the 1960s, communications satellites came into use (see SATELLITE). Communications satellites relay telephone signals that have been converted into radio waves (see RADIO). Communications satellites are used for long-distance telephone calls, especially overseas. They can handle tens of thousands of calls at one time. In contrast, a copper wire can usually only

**TELEPHONE STATION**
The tower of this special telephone station has many antennas for sending and receiving telephone messages by radio.

handle one call at a time. Converting telephone signals into light signals through the use of tiny laser beams came into use in the early 1980s. The laser beams travel along hair-thin glass tubes called optical fibers (see FIBER OPTICS; LASER). Optical fibers are much smaller than copper wires and can handle about one thousand calls each. In addition, the use of light means there is no electrical interference.

## How a modern telephone works

Today's transmitters work in much the same way that Edison's worked. However, the electricity for today's telephones is supplied by batteries at the telephone company. The electric signals travel from the transmitter to a special station. At the station, the electric signals may be converted into other forms, such as light or radio waves. The signals travel in these other forms for much of the distance to the receiving telephone. Before actually reaching the receiving telephone, the signals reach a final station. There, they are converted back into electric signals. The electric signals travel over wire to the receiving telephone.

The receiving telephone has a diaphragm and two magnets. One magnet continually pulls on the diaphragm. The other magnet is surrounded by a coil of wire. When an electric signal travels through this second magnet, it becomes an electromagnet. The electromagnet then pulls on the diaphragm. Its

### MOBILE TELEPHONE

Mobile telephones, also called cellular telephones, work using radio waves. Signals from the caller's telephone are sent from the telephone's antenna to a radio receiver. The signals are then passed on to the receiving telephone, either by wire or by radio waves.

pull is opposite to the pull of the regular magnet. The opposing pulls cause the diaphragm to vibrate according to the signal. The vibration produces sound.

## Modern telephone systems

Modern telephone systems have changed the way conversations are held. For example, many telephones today are mobile. They can be carried in a pocket or installed in a car. Mobile telephones are also called cellular telephones. This is because the area in which a mobile telephone is located is called a cell. Mobile telephones work by radio waves. The electric signals from the mobile telephone are converted into radio waves and sent by an antenna to a radio receiver (see ANTENNA). The receiver may be in the same cell from which the call has been made or another cell, depending on where the call is being made to. The receiver converts the radio waves into electric signals. The signals travel to a station. If the call is being made to a noncellular telephone, the signals are either sent directly to a telephone or first converted into light signals and sent over optical fibers to another station. If the call is being made to another cellular telephone, the signals are sent to a transmitter to be converted into radio waves. The radio waves are then received by the antenna of the cellular telephone. The cellular telephone's receiver converts the radio waves into electric signals.

Some telephones today also allow a person to see the person with whom he or she is talking. These videophones are used with a kind of video camera and video screen (see TELEVISION).

Modern telephone systems are used for other kinds of communication besides conversation. For example, a device called a modem allows information to be sent from computer to computer using telephone systems (see COMPUTER; MODEM). A person who works away from his or her office, such as a salesperson, can communicate with other workers in the office by using a modem and a telephone system. A telephone system can also be used to send copies of handwritten or typed material, maps, photographs, or other art using a facsimile (fax) machine. *See also* FACSIMILE MACHINE; SOUND; TELECOMMUNICATION.

PROJECT 48

The telescope is an instrument used to observe and study objects that are a great distance away. The Dutch scientist Hans Lippershey invented the telescope in 1608. In 1609, the Italian scientist Galileo made his first telescope. Galileo was the first person to use a telescope to observe the heavens (see GALILEO). Galileo soon discovered the rings of Saturn, four of Jupiter's moons, the phases of Venus, and the mountains and craters on Earth's moon. Today, there are two main kinds of telescopes—optical telescopes and radio telescopes. Optical telescopes observe visible light being sent from bodies in space. Radio telescopes detect radio waves being sent from space. The two main kinds of optical telescopes are refracting and reflecting. Refracting telescopes use lenses, while reflecting telescopes use mirrors. A third type of optical telescope, called a catadioptric telescope, combines the techniques of refracting and reflecting telescopes.

## Refracting telescopes

A refracting telescope is a closed tube. At the viewing end of the tube is a small eyepiece, called the ocular. At the other end of the tube is a lens called the objective (see CONVEX; LENS). The objective refracts, or bends, light from the object being viewed to form an image in the eyepiece (see REFRACTION OF LIGHT).

A Keplerian telescope is a refracting telescope with a convex eyepiece and a larger convex lens for the objective. The image produced by a Keplerian telescope is upside down. The Keplerian telescope is the refracting telescope used by most astronomers (scientists who study heavenly bodies).

Modern refracting telescopes usually contain complicated lens systems. These systems correct certain aberrations, such as chromatic aberrations, that the design of refracting telescopes naturally causes (see ABERRATION). A system of lenses also makes a refracting telescope especially useful in detecting the distance from Earth and the size of heavenly bodies. One of the world's largest refracting telescopes is at the Yerkes Observatory in Wisconsin. The objective there is 40 in. [102 cm] in diameter.

## Reflecting telescopes

The reflecting telescope was developed to avoid the aberrations of the refracting telescope. The reflecting telescope is especially useful in studying the spectrum of light sent from heavenly bodies. From the spectrum, astronomers can determine different properties of a heavenly body, such as its chemical composition

### ASTRONOMICAL TELESCOPES

There are various types of reflecting astronomical telescopes. The Newtonian telescope is an early design that uses a curved (concave) mirror, with a flat mirror to reflect light rays into the eyepiece. The Schmidt telescope has a mirror and a large lens, as does the similarly designed Matsukov telescope.

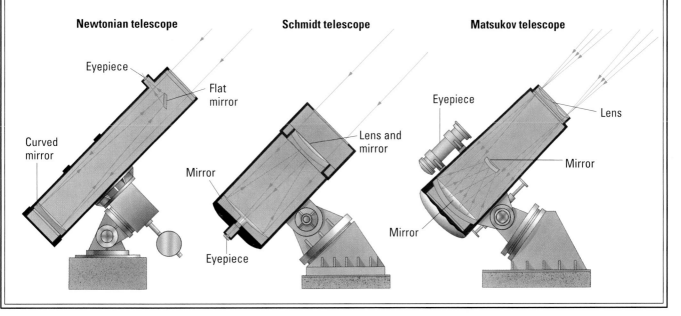

**Newtonian telescope**
Eyepiece
Flat mirror
Curved mirror

**Schmidt telescope**
Lens and mirror
Mirror
Eyepiece

**Matsukov telescope**
Eyepiece
Lens
Mirror
Mirror

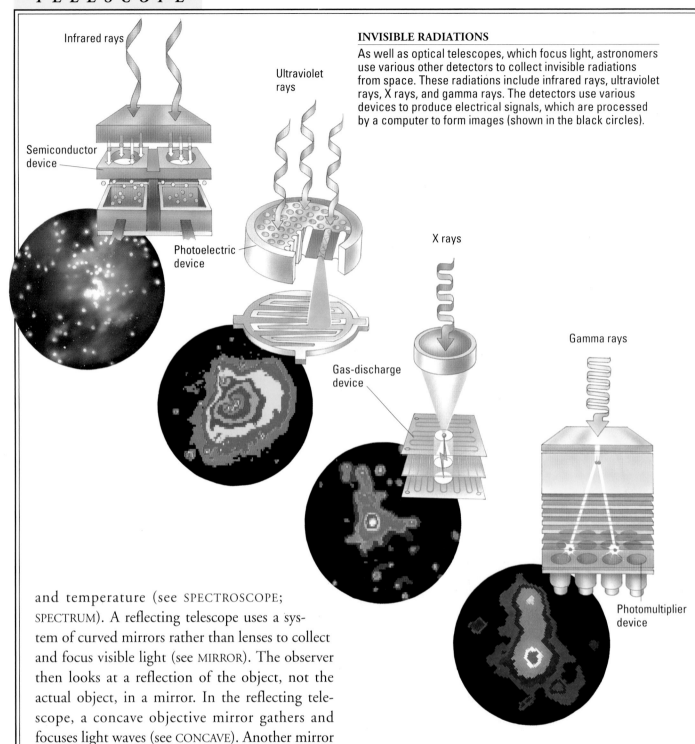

Infrared rays

Semiconductor
device

Ultraviolet
rays

Photoelectric
device

X rays

Gas-discharge
device

Gamma rays

Photomultiplier
device

As well as optical telescopes, which focus light, astronomers use various other detectors to collect invisible radiations from space. These radiations include infrared rays, ultraviolet rays, X rays, and gamma rays. The detectors use various devices to produce electrical signals, which are processed by a computer to form images (shown in the black circles).

and temperature (see SPECTROSCOPE; SPECTRUM). A reflecting telescope uses a system of curved mirrors rather than lenses to collect and focus visible light (see MIRROR). The observer then looks at a reflection of the object, not the actual object, in a mirror. In the reflecting telescope, a concave objective mirror gathers and focuses light waves (see CONCAVE). Another mirror near the point where the waves come together reflects the light into the eyepiece (see REFLECTION OF LIGHT). Sir Isaac Newton built the first reflecting telescope (see NEWTON, SIR ISAAC).

N. Cassegrain of France invented another kind of reflecting telescope in 1672. A Cassegrainian telescope has an objective that is a large concave mirror with a hole in the middle. The objective is located behind another, small mirror. The eyepiece is behind the objective. As light strikes the

objective, it is reflected back to the small mirror and then passed through the hole to form an image in the eyepiece. This design helps correct for a kind of aberration called spherical aberration.

The largest reflecting telescope is the Keck Telescope. The Keck is located on top of Mauna Kea, an extinct volcano in Hawaii. Its objective mirror, which is actually made up of many smaller mirrors, is about 400 in. [10 m] in diameter. The largest reflecting telescope with an objective mirror that is a single piece can be found at the Special Astrophysical Observatory in Russia. Its objective mirror is 236 in. [600 cm.] in diameter. The Palomar Observatory in California contains the Hale Telescope. The Hale Telescope is the largest single-mirror reflecting telescope in North America. It has an objective mirror that is 200 in. [508 cm] in diameter.

The Palomar Observatory also has one of the largest catadioptric telescopes. Called the Schmidt Telescope, it has a lens that is 48 in. [122 cm] in diameter and an objective mirror that is 72 in. [183 cm] in diameter.

Optical telescopes are seldom used for direct observation. Instead, astronomers study photographs taken of the image. These photographs are processed in such a way that light images too dim to be seen by the human eye will show up on the film. Any vibrations that occur while the photographs are being taken will blur the image. Therefore, the mounting of the mirrors and lenses is very important.

Optical telescopes are often located in buildings called observatories. These observatories are usually built at high altitudes, such as mountain peaks, and away from large cities (see OBSERVATORY). This minimizes any dimming effects of pollution and the glare of city lights.

Because of the tremendous amount of light and heat that the sun sends to Earth, a special kind of reflecting telescope, called a solar telescope, was developed to study it. Solar telescopes are often large structures that are fixed toward one direction. The McMath solar telescope at Kitt Peak, Arizona, is over 500 ft. [152 m] long. Two-thirds of the telescope extends underground, where it is cooled. The cooling helps protect the telescope from the intense heat of the sun as its light passes through the telescope. Most of the mirrors and photographic equipment are located in the underground part of the telescope. The other one-third of the telescope extends toward the sky and contains an objective mirror that is 80 in. [203 cm] in diameter. This mirror is located 100 ft. [30 m] above ground level. This is to avoid distortions in the image caused by

the sun's energy being reflected when it hits the ground. The McMath telescope gives an image of the sun that is 3 ft. [0.9 m] across. Another way to reduce the problem of heat distortion is to create a vacuum inside the telescope (see VACUUM). The solar telescope at Sacramento Peak Observatory in New Mexico has all air removed from the entire telescope.

**Radio telescopes** A radio telescope has a huge bowl-shaped reflector, often called a dish. The reflector collects and focuses radio waves on the antenna (see ANTENNA). The antenna changes the radio waves into electrical signals. A receiver picks up and amplifies (strengthens) the signals that the astronomer wishes to study.

Radio telescopes are useful in studying objects that give off no visible light but do give off radio waves. Radio telescopes also can be used at any time of the day or night and in all kinds of weather, unlike optical telescopes. Radio telescopes are usually located in valleys to minimize any interference from radio waves being given off by objects on Earth.

**REFLECTING TELESCOPE**

The astronomical telescope at the observatory on Mauna Kea, Hawaii, has a main mirror 88 in. [216 cm] across.

**ORBITING TELESCOPE**

The Hubble Space Telescope is an astronomical telescope in orbit around Earth. Because it is above the earth's atmosphere, it takes clearer pictures than telescopes on the ground.

The Arecibo Observatory in Puerto Rico has one of the world's largest radio telescopes. The reflector is 1,000 ft. [305 m] in diameter. A similar telescope with a reflector 2,000 ft. [610 m] in diameter has been built in Russia. A type of radio telescope called a radio interferometer uses two or more reflectors in a line (see INTERFEROMETER). A radio interferometer called the Very Large Array in New Mexico has twenty-seven reflectors arranged in the shape of a *Y*. Each reflector is 82 ft. [25 m] in diameter (see RADIO ASTRONOMY).

**Space telescopes** Ultraviolet, X-ray, and gamma ray observations can only be made from spacecraft because they cannot be observed through the Earth's atmosphere. Since the 1960s, the National Aeronautics and Space Administration (NASA) has placed more than seventy telescopes into space (see NASA). Many of these are no longer operating but remain in space. The orbiting telescopes have the advantage of being able to operate both day and night. They can view space and detect both light and radio waves without any interference from the earth's atmosphere or from pollution. Also, they can detect X rays and certain ultraviolet rays. These signals cannot be detected on Earth because they are absorbed by the earth's atmosphere (see INFRARED RAY; ULTRAVIOLET RAY).

The largest reflecting space telescope is the Hubble Space Telescope (HST). It has an objective mirror that is 94 in. [239 cm] in diameter. It was placed into orbit in 1990. An error in the way one of the mirrors was manufactured caused some of the first images sent to Earth to be distorted. Astronauts repaired the telescope in 1993. This resulted in dramatically improved images.

NASA has plans for two X-ray telescopes to be sent into orbit in the 1990s, and has also proposed a space telescope that would detect infrared rays. *See also* ASTRONOMY; MOON; PLANET; UNIVERSE.

Television is a means by which moving pictures and sound are sent and received electronically. Television allows viewers to see and hear distant scenes and events. Television brings news, entertainment, and education to millions of people.

**A brief history** Early ideas about television involved transmitting, or sending, the entire picture through the air at once. In 1880, W.E. Sawyer in the United States and Maurice Leblanc in France independently came up with an important improvement. Sawyer and Leblanc suggested that a picture be split up and transmitted as a large number of signals, one after another. In 1923, the Russian-American scientist Vladimir Zworykin developed a device for splitting up a picture and transmitting the signals. His device combined a photoelectric cell and a cathode-ray tube (see CATHODE-RAY TUBE; PHOTOELECTRIC EFFECT). This was the first television camera tube. That same year, Zworykin also used a cathode-ray tube to develop the first television picture tube. In 1929, Zworykin demonstrated his camera and picture tube as part of the first practical television system. Experimental broadcasting continued in the 1930s. (Broadcasting is the transmission of radio or television signals.) The world's first public television service began in 1936 with the British Broadcasting Corporation (BBC) broadcasts from London, England. The first regular television broadcasts in the United States occurred in 1939. Television broadcasting in the United States was suspended from 1941 until 1945 because of U.S. involvement in World War II (1939–1945). In the late 1940s and 1950s, television broadcasting as a form of entertainment greatly increased, as did the demand for it by the American people.

**How television works** A television camera works similarly to a regular camera that takes still photographs (see CAMERA; PHOTOGRAPHY). However, a television camera does not use film to capture the image. Instead, it captures the image as electronic signals. Like a regular camera, a television camera takes pictures by using a lens to capture the rays of light that pass into it (see LENS). As the light from the scene is passing into the camera, sound from the scene is passing into a microphone. The microphone changes the sound into electronic signals called audio signals (see MICROPHONE). Depending on the camera, three dichroic mirrors or three filters inside the camera divide the light coming into the camera into three parts (see MIRROR). One mirror or one filter allows only

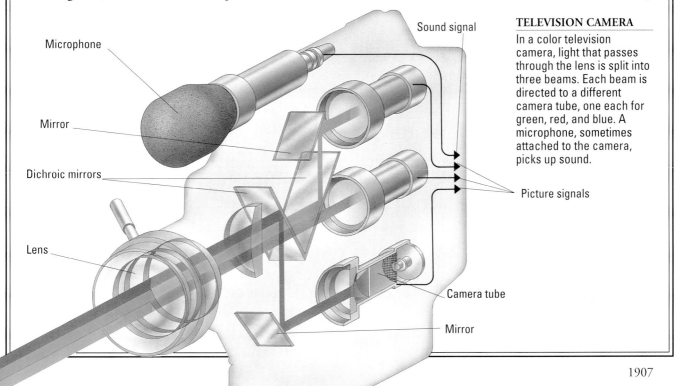

Microphone

Mirror

Dichroic mirrors

Lens

Sound signal

Picture signals

Camera tube

Mirror

**TELEVISION CAMERA**
In a color television camera, light that passes through the lens is split into three beams. Each beam is directed to a different camera tube, one each for green, red, and blue. A microphone, sometimes attached to the camera, picks up sound.

red-colored light to pass. The second mirror or filter allows only blue-colored light to pass. The third mirror or filter allows only green-colored light to pass (see COLOR). Each color goes to a different camera tube. (In a camera that will eventually produce only black-and-white images, there is only one camera tube and no mirrors or filters.) Each tube has a glass plate called a faceplate at one end. In the back of the faceplate is a transparent (see-through) coating called a signal plate. Behind the signal plate is another plate called the target. The target is coated with a layer of photoconductive material. A material that is photoconductive converts light energy into electric signals. At the end of the tube opposite the target is a device called an electron gun. An electron gun emits (gives off) electrons. Electrons are particles that have a negative electric charge (see ELECTRICITY; ELECTRON).

When the television camera is in operation, each of the three colors of light passes through its appropriate faceplate and signal plate. The light shines on the target. This causes electrons in the target's photoconductive material to move toward the signal plate. This movement causes the back of the target plate to be left with a positive electric charge. The strength of the electric charge is determined by the brightness of the light from the image. In this way, the charge captures an electronic pattern of the original image. The electron gun emits a stream of electrons across the back of the target. Magnets located near the stream of electrons affect the direction of the electrons by attracting and repelling

them. This attraction and repulsion forces the electrons into a steady beam that is directed at the target. The magnets also make the beam travel in a line, from left to right, across the target. This is called scanning. In the United States, there are 525 lines on the target. When the beam scans all the lines, it has completed a "frame." The beam completes a frame thirty times a second. In other countries, pictures are made up using 625 or 819 lines, with 25 images per second. As the beam is scanning, it hits areas that have different amounts of positive charge, depending on the amount of light from the image that was focused on it. Areas with strong charges attract the most electrons from the beam. Areas with weak charges attract fewer electrons. The electrons that are attracted move through the target. They then cause an electric current to flow through the signal plate. The voltage of the current depends on the amount of electrons that are passing through (see CURRENT, ELECTRIC; VOLT). The changing voltage forms a video signal.

The video signals as well as the signals from the microphone may be recorded on videotape or, sometimes, on motion picture film to be viewed later (see MOTION PICTURE; VIDEO RECORDING). The scene may also be viewed "live," or as it happens. The recorded signals or the "live" signals pass by wire to a device called a transmitter, or sender. The transmitter adds radio waves called carrier waves to both the video and audio signals for them to travel on (see RADIO). The video signals are sent from the transmitter by amplitude modulation (AM). In AM transmission, the amplitude

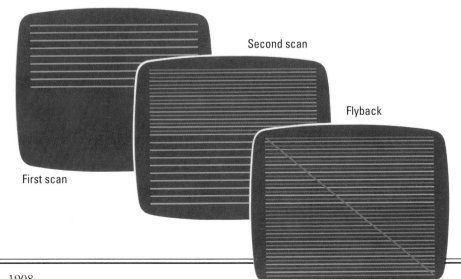

First scan

Second scan

Flyback

### SCANNING

The pictures on a television screen are made up of horizontal lines produced by an electron beam scanning the face of the picture tube. First lines 1, 3, 5, 7, and so on are scanned from top to bottom. Then lines 2, 4, 6, 8, and so on are drawn between them to complete the picture. Finally the electron beam flies back to the beginning to repeat the process for the next picture.

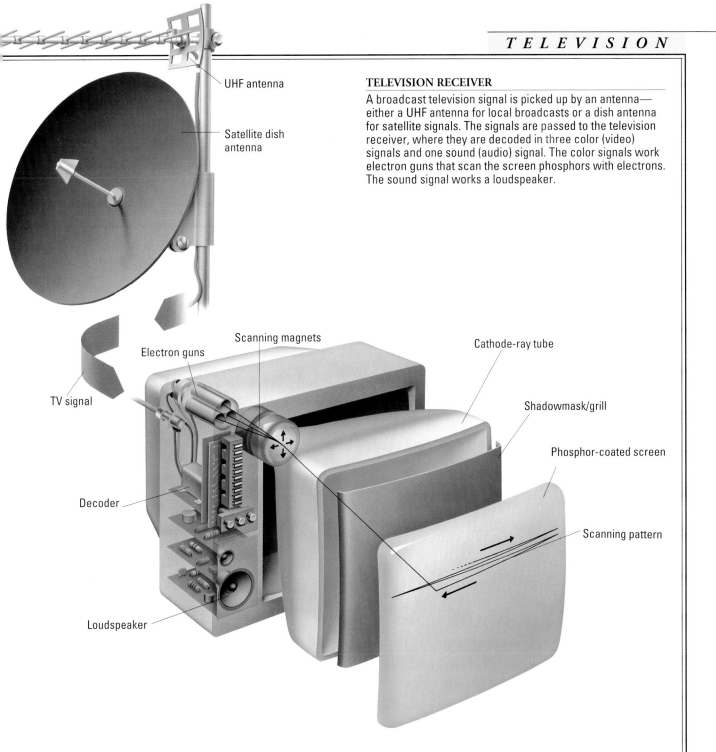

UHF antenna

Satellite dish antenna

**TELEVISION RECEIVER**
A broadcast television signal is picked up by an antenna—either a UHF antenna for local broadcasts or a dish antenna for satellite signals. The signals are passed to the television receiver, where they are decoded in three color (video) signals and one sound (audio) signal. The color signals work electron guns that scan the screen phosphors with electrons. The sound signal works a loudspeaker.

Scanning magnets

Electron guns

Cathode-ray tube

Shadowmask/grill

TV signal

Phosphor-coated screen

Decoder

Scanning pattern

Loudspeaker

(strength) of the carrier waves varies to match changes in the video signals (see AMPLITUDE). The audio signals are sent from the transmitter by frequency modulation (FM). In FM transmission, the frequency of the carrier waves changes to match the audio signals (see FREQUENCY). The AM and FM signals are combined in a process known as modulation to form one television signal. The television signal is sent from the transmitter over wire to a transmitting antenna. The transmitting antenna sends the signal through the air. When this signal reaches a home television antenna, the antenna

turns the waves back into electric signals. The electric signals travel to the television set, or receiver. Electronic circuits in the set separate the video signals from the audio signals. The video signals travel into the part of the television set called a cathode-ray tube. The cathode-ray tube has one end that is flat and almost square in shape. The cathode-ray tube is more commonly called the picture tube. The picture tube converts the video signals into patterns of light that match the original signals from the camera tubes. The audio signals travel to a loudspeaker. The loudspeaker converts the electric signals back into sound (see LOUDSPEAKER).

Similar to a television camera tube, the picture tube has an electron gun. Color televisions have three electron guns for the three color signals. A black-and-white picture tube has only one electron gun. Magnets direct the electrons from the electron gun into a beam that hits the inside of the flat end of the picture tube. In a color tube, this end is coated with fluorescent dots that glow a certain color—blue, green, or red—when struck by electrons (see FLUORESCENCE). In a black-and-white tube, the dots glow with only different amounts of white light. Just as in the television camera, in the United States, each electron beam travels across the flat end of the picture tube 525 times, completing thirty frames a second. The eye translates the glowing dots into a complete picture. The eye does not see the individual spots, because the electron beam moves too fast. However, if one looks closely at a television picture, the 525 lines that run across the tube can be seen.

Scientists have developed televisions that have more lines and, thus, produce a sharper and more colorful image. These televisions are called high-definition televisions, or HDTVs.

**Television broadcasting today** Almost every home in the United States has at least one television set. Most of them are color sets. Scientists estimate that each home uses its television about seven hours a day. Programs, such as entertainment or news shows, can be sent to the television set through the air from local stations or by underground cables from cable television systems.

In 1993, there were over 1,500 local television stations in the United States. About 1,150 of these local stations are commercial stations. A commercial station receives most of its funding from sponsors in return for broadcasting advertisements for the sponsors' products. These advertisements, called commercials, are broadcast during and between programs. About 75 percent of the commercial stations receive most of their programming from one of four national networks. These commercial stations are called affiliates. The rest of the commercial stations operate independently.

About 350 of the 1,500 local stations are public stations. Public stations receive funding from several different sources, such as viewer contributions, state or local taxes, or government grants. Public stations are not affiliates of one of the national networks. They may create their own programs or buy

**TELEVISION NEWS**
Television can broadcast up-to-date news programs as, or immediately after, events happen. A camera operator (above) "captures" the event, which is relayed to the studio and transmitted as part of a news broadcast (left).

programs produced by other stations or individuals. Public stations generally provide programs that are educational and cultural in nature.

All local television stations broadcast their programs on a specific frequency. The viewer chooses this frequency when he or she selects a specific channel on the television set.

There are about 11,000 cable television systems in the United States. Cable television was originally only for those areas that had trouble receiving signals sent through the air. These areas include isolated communities, mountain valleys, and areas with many tall buildings. However, cable television has become popular in many other areas because it can carry many television signals. For example, a cable television system may carry programs from the four national networks as well as many other special features. These features may include continuous news or weather shows or sports events not broadcast by the national networks. A person must pay an installation fee and a monthly service fee to receive cable television.

Some programs broadcast by air or through cables can be viewed only after paying a special fee. These programs are called pay television programs. For example, pay television operators may transmit scrambled television signals through the air. A person who has paid the required fee attaches a special unscrambling device to his or her television. The device allows him or her to view the program. In cable television systems, a viewer is not able to receive a specific channel, such as one that shows motion pictures that have never been shown on television before, unless he or she has paid an extra fee. Often, this fee is paid monthly.

Today, many families are using their televisions as parts of home entertainment centers. In addition to a television, the entertainment center may contain a videocassette recorder/player (VCR), laser disc player (also known as a videodisc player), high-fidelity sound system, and/or personal computer. Some families are even purchasing television and computer combinations (see COMPUTER; RECORDING; SOUND RECORDING; VIDEO RECORDING).

With a home VCR, a program can be preserved on videotape for viewing at a later time. In fact, the VCR can tape a program being broadcast on one channel while another channel is being viewed on the screen. The VCR can also be used for playing commercially prerecorded tapes, such as tapes of movies, which can be bought or rented. Laser disc players are used in a similar manner as VCRs. However, the laser discs used in laser disc players are not recordable. A high-fidelity system can be used when the sound of a television program is broadcast in stereo. A person can choose the specific radio channel over which the sound is being broadcast. The person then hears the sound in stereo coming from the speakers of the high-fidelity system. Some televisions today are able to broadcast programs that have been recorded in stereo. Many personal computers make use of television screens as monitors. A family may use the personal computer for such activities as playing games or keeping track of household expenses.

Related equipment for the home entertainment center may include a portable video camera/recorder, called a camcorder; a projection television; or a personal television. The camcorder works in a manner similar to a television camera and records events on cassettes. These events can later be viewed on the television using the VCR. The projection television, also called a big-screen TV, works in a manner similar to a regular television. However, instead of the video signals being displayed on a picture tube, they are displayed on a large screen similar to a movie screen. Projection televisions are often used in public places to view sports events. Personal televisions are small portable televisions that may be powered by batteries.

Television cameras and sets that operate on a closed circuit have made an impact in business, medicine, and education. A closed-circuit system sends television signals over wires to a limited number of television sets. A closed-circuit system can be used to watch different areas of stores and banks. This helps prevent shoplifting and robbery. A closed-circuit system allows nurses to watch several patients simultaneously. A closed-circuit system can be used in schools to have several classrooms view a lesson that is being taught in only one classroom. *See also* ELECTRONICS.

**TELLER, EDWARD** (1908– ) Edward Teller is a famous nuclear scientist. Largely because of his research, the hydrogen bomb was developed in 1952. Teller is often called the "father of the hydrogen bomb" (see ATOM; NUCLEAR WEAPONS).

Teller was born in Budapest, Hungary. He received his doctoral degree in physics from the University of Leipzig in Germany, in 1932. Teller moved to the United States in 1935. He became a U.S. citizen in 1941.

During World War II (1939–1945), Teller assisted in the U.S. research effort called the Manhattan Project. The Manhattan Project was responsible for the development of the first atomic bomb. During the early 1950s, Teller began work on developing the hydrogen bomb. The first hydrogen bomb was tested in the Pacific Ocean in 1952. Unlike the atomic bomb, the hydrogen bomb has not yet been used in warfare.

In the early 1950s, Teller helped found the Lawrence Livermore National Laboratory in California. This laboratory is mainly involved in developing nuclear weapons. From 1958 to 1960, Teller was director of the laboratory. He was its associate director from 1972 to 1975. He was also a professor of physics at the University of California at Berkeley from 1953 to 1975.

**TEMPERATURE** Temperature is a measure of how hot a body or substance is. Temperature is measured with a thermometer. A thermometer has a scale (a series of numbered marks) that indicates the level of heat in degrees Fahrenheit or Celsius. Extremely high temperatures can be measured with a device called a pyrometer (see CELSIUS SCALE; DEGREE; FAHRENHEIT SCALE; PYROMETER; THERMOMETER). Temperature is also the measure of the kinetic energy of the molecules that make up the body or substance. Kinetic energy is the energy of motion of the molecules (see KINETIC ENERGY; MOLECULE). When energy is added to an object, the molecules speed up, and the object gets hotter. For example, energy is added to a liquid as it is stirred, to a gas as it is squeezed, and to a solid as it is hammered. A thermometer shows this increase in kinetic energy as a rise in temperature.

Most scientists believe that there is no upper limit to temperature. However, there is a lower limit. It is called absolute zero, and it occurs at -459.67°F [-273.15 °C]. At absolute zero, the molecules of a body or material are motionless. They have no kinetic energy.
*See also* ABSOLUTE ZERO; HEAT.　　PROJECT 45

**TEMPERATURE, BODY** An animal's body temperature is a measurement of its body heat. An animal generates heat through respiration. However, an animal also loses heat to, and gains heat from, its environment (see ENVIRONMENT; HEAT; RESPIRATION).

Mammals and birds are called warm-blooded animals. The body temperature of a warm-blooded animal usually stays about the same. It is affected very little by the temperature of the environment.

**TEMPERATURE, BODY**

The internal body temperature of a human being usually stays about the same. But the surface temperature (temperature on the skin) varies from place to place on the body. The variation can be seen on this thermogram, in which the lightest color represents the highest temperature.

This is because a warm-blooded animal's body can balance the amount of heat it gives to the environment with the amount it generates. All other animals are called cold-blooded. Their body temperatures vary and are usually close to the temperature of the environment (see BIRD; COLD-BLOODED ANIMAL; MAMMAL; WARM-BLOODED ANIMAL).

In humans, the normal body temperature is about 98.6°F [37°C]. Children may have a slightly higher body temperature. During the day, the body temperature of a human varies by about 1.8°F [1°C]. The temperature is lowest in the morning. It rises throughout the day and peaks in late afternoon. It then begins to lower and continues dropping throughout the night. Strenuous exercise can cause the body temperature to rise slightly. In very hot or very cold weather, skin temperature may differ a great deal from the body's internal temperature.

In women, the menstrual cycle causes slight temperature changes every month (see MENSTRUAL CYCLE). The body temperature is usually lower during the first half of the cycle. In addition, the body temperature drops slightly, rises about 1.8°F [1°C], then drops slightly again at about the time of ovulation (the release of an egg from an ovary).

Many diseases cause a fever (see DISEASE; FEVER). Diseases usually cause fever by activating immune system cells. These cells release chemicals that act on control centers in the central nervous system to increase body temperature (see IMMUNITY; NERVOUS SYSTEM). Some pathogens (disease-causing organisms) are killed by even a small increase in a person's body temperature. If the body temperature rises above 111.2°F [44°C], however, some important enzymes are destroyed, and death often results. *See also* ENZYME.

**TENDON** Tendons are connective tissues that attach muscles to bones. They look like strong, white cords and are made of densely packed bundles of collagen. Tendons are enclosed in a layer of protective tissue.
*See also* BONE; COLLAGEN; CONNECTIVE TISSUE; MUSCLE.

**TENDRIL** (tĕn'drəl) A tendril is the part of a climbing plant that attaches itself to an object for support. Some may be modified stems, but most are modified leaves or parts of leaves. They are usually very slender, and they quickly coil, or wrap themselves, around twigs or other means of support (see CLIMBING PLANT).

Some tendrils have a great deal of elasticity, or ability to stretch and turn without breaking. This keeps them from snapping in strong winds. The tendrils of the Virginia creeper do not coil around supports. Instead, the tendrils are branched structures. Each branch has a tiny sucker pad that attaches the plant to a wall or other surface.
*See also* VIRGINIA CREEPER.

**TENDRIL**
Sweet peas climb up a support using tendrils, which in these plants are modified leaves.

**TENSION** When a string or wire is stretched, it is said to be in tension. The forces that are stretching the string or wire are tension forces. Another name for a tension or stretching force is tensile stress (see STRESS AND STRAIN). A tent is held up by tension in the ropes and fabric of the tent. The strings of a guitar are in tension. The tension force in a guitar string is changed by turning a peg attached to one end of the string. As the tension changes, the note made by the string when it is plucked changes.

## TERMINAL VELOCITY (tûr′mə nəl və lŏs′ ĭ tē)

When a body falls through the air, air resistance always tends to slow it down. The faster a body falls, the greater the air resistance. If the body is dropped from a great enough height, it at first accelerates (gains speed) as it falls. Eventually, however, the air resistance becomes so great that the body cannot increase its speed any more. It is then traveling at its terminal velocity. A body can reach a terminal velocity when falling through any gas or liquid.

*See also* GRAVITY.

## TERMITE

Termites are social insects that belong to the order Isoptera. Although they are sometimes called "white ants," termites and ants are not closely related (see ANT). Unlike ants, most termites have thick waists and soft, pale bodies. The length of a termite's body is from 0.1 to 0.7 in. [2.5 to 18 mm]. The main food of termites is cellulose, a major substance in the cell walls of plants (see CELLULOSE). With the help of special bacteria, protozoans, and fungi in their intestines, most termites are able to digest cellulose (see BACTERIA; PROTOZOA). Because of this ability, termites can cause great damage to books, furniture, buildings, and many other objects that contain cellulose.

Of the two thousand known species, only about forty live in North America. Most other species live in tropical areas, where they are an important part

### TERMITE—Inside the nest

A termite nest has ventilation shafts to let in cool air and get rid of stale air. Soldier termites stand on guard outside, while workers tend the queen and her eggs in the brood chamber. Winged males develop only when a female termite leaves to start a new nest.

### TERMITE—Outside the nest

From the outside, a termite nest is a rugged "tower" of rock-hard soil up to 20 ft. [6 m] tall (right). The nest also extends up to 10 ft. [3 m] underground.

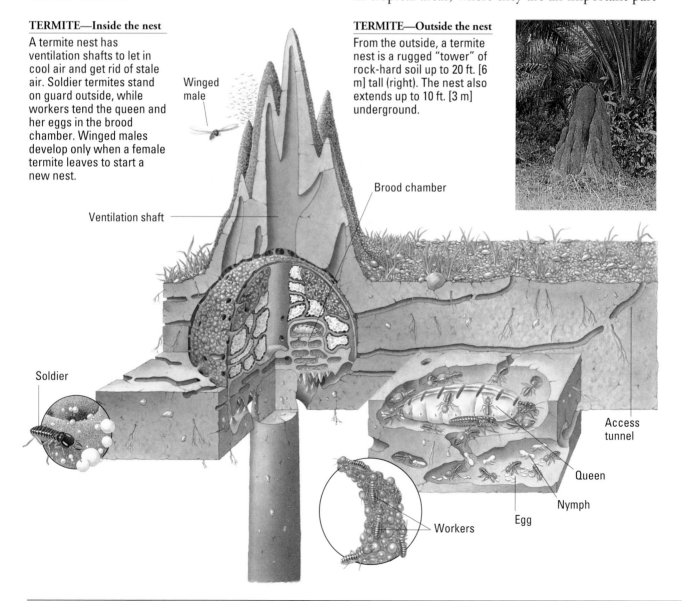

Winged male

Brood chamber

Ventilation shaft

Soldier

Access tunnel

Queen

Nymph

Egg

Workers

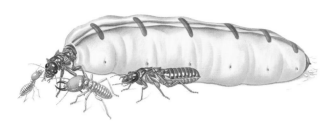

**TERMITE—Queen**
The huge queen termite, containing thousands of eggs, dwarfs the darker king and the even smaller workers.

of the food chain (see FOOD CHAIN). They help change dead trees into new soil.

There are seven families of termites, but over three quarters of the species belong to the family Termitidae. Among these are the black mound termites (genus *Amitermes*). They build huge, waterproof nests that look like small mountains. These nests are so hard that they produce sparks if hit with an ax. The black mound termites never leave the nest above the ground, but rather tunnel to get food. They usually eat rotten wood.

The damp-wood termites (family Rhinotermitidae) usually live in dead wood, underground or lying on the surface. They are the smallest and most destructive of the termites. They die if they lose contact with soil moisture, but they sometimes build covered walkways with soil and cleared wood so that they can reach new feeding grounds safely. The dry-wood termites (family Kalotermitidae) live in dry or damp wood, above or below the ground. They stay in their nests and feed on the wood until it is reduced to dust. In the United States, these termites are found along the west coast, in the deserts of the southwest, and in the southeast. The harvester termites (family Hodotermitidae) leave their nests in search of living grasses and other plants.

Most termite colonies (communities) have three castes, or groups: reproductives (those who produce eggs), workers, and soldiers. Termites are the only social insects with workers and soldiers of both sexes. All young termites are the same at first, and scientists do not know for sure why some become reproductives while others are sterile (unable to reproduce) workers and soldiers. It is thought, however, that this development is controlled by food, hormones, or pheromones (see HORMONE; LARVA; PHEROMONE).

The reproductive, or royal, caste is made up of fully developed fertile males and females. They have hard, dark bodies; weak eyes; and four wings each. Each colony is started by a pair of reproductives—one king and one queen. Once the colony has been started and before they mate, the king and queen shed their wings.

The workers are either sterile adults or, in some species, nymphs (see NYMPH). They are blind and have soft, pale, wingless bodies. They do all the work in the colony, such as making the nest larger, feeding the other termites, and caring for the eggs. The workers are the most numerous members of the colony. The soldiers are larger than the workers. They also are blind and have soft, wingless bodies. They have large, powerful heads and strong jaws, however. Their main function is to protect the other termites in case of an attack. Soldiers cannot feed or care for themselves and must depend on the workers for assistance.

The king and queen live in a small space in the center of the nest, and they mate periodically. The queen's body becomes huge as she begins producing thousands of eggs every day. A single queen may lay eggs at the rate of three thousand per day for as long as fifty years. As she lays the eggs, the workers carry them off. The fertilized eggs are brought to cells (rooms) where they develop into nymphs, some of which develop into reproductive adults. Every year, the young reproductives swarm out of the nest. Most are eaten by birds and other animals, but a few will form new colonies.

*See also* INSECT; METAMORPHOSIS.

**TERN** A tern is a bird that belongs to the family Sternidae. It is closely related to the gulls and is usually white with gray or black wings. Some terns are completely black or gray. The wings are long, narrow, and pointed. The tail of the tern is usually forked. The bill is much more slender than that of a gull.

There are fourteen species of terns native to North America. They range in length from 8 to 20 in. [21 to 50 cm]. Most terns live near the ocean. A

### TERN

Various species of terns are found throughout the world, living near oceans or inland seas. Pictured here are the Arctic tern (top left), the Inca tern (bottom left), and the Caspian tern (below).

few species live inland, near large rivers or lakes. Terns eat small fish and sometimes insects. They are very agile fliers and dive into the water to capture fish. Terns fly along the water in large flocks, following schools (groups) of fish.
*See also* BIRD.

**TERRAPIN** (tĕr'ə pĭn) *Terrapin* is the name that is sometimes applied to any freshwater turtle, such as members of genus *Pseudemys.* These turtles live

### TERRAPIN

A terrapin is any type of freshwater turtle. Here a male red-eared turtle courts the larger female by waving his claws near her face.

in ponds and streams from New England to South America. In the United States, *terrapin* usually refers to the diamondback terrapin. This turtle lives in coastal waters and salt marshes from Massachusetts to Texas. The female is larger than the male, sometimes measuring 8 in. [20 cm] across. The diamondback terrapin feeds on small water plants and animals.
*See also* TURTLE.

**TERRITORY** A territory is an area occupied by an individual or a group of animals of the same species and defended against other animals of the same kind. By adopting and defending territories, the animals ensure that they have enough food for themselves and their offspring. Many mammals use scent to mark the boundaries of their territories and warn others to keep away (see MAMMAL). Gibbons and howler monkeys defend their territories with sound (see MONKEY). They call loudly early in the morning and in the evening to let other families know that the territory is occupied. Small fights sometimes occur at the boundaries of the territories, but serious fights are rare. Unless the defender is getting old or ill, it usually manages to turn away the intruder.

Some animals, especially large carnivores, have territories covering many square miles (see CARNIVORE). They need big territories in order to find enough food, but they can manage with smaller territories when food is plentiful. Leaf-eating monkeys defend smaller territories than fruit-eating monkeys because they can always find enough leaves.

Many animals, especially birds, establish territories only for the mating season (see BIRD). The male birds usually establish the territories. Their songs attract females but usually drive other males away. Those birds whose territories contain the best nesting sites often raise the most offspring. If a stranger enters the territory, the occupier puts on an aggressive display to drive it away. The red-winged blackbird, for example, displays its patches of bright red and yellow wing feathers as a warning. If the intruder still does not retreat, the occupier will attack it and chase it out of the territory.

Some territories are held for long periods, especially when the animals are looking after nests and young, but some may be changed every day. Howler monkeys, for example, claim whatever area of the forest they find themselves in, as long as it is not already occupied. The European speckled wood butterfly changes its territory several times a day (see BUTTERFLY). The territory is just a patch of sunlight, perhaps only a few feet across, to which the male butterfly hopes a female will be attracted. As the day progresses and the territory becomes shaded, the butterfly moves to other sunny spots.

Many animals keep to fairly definite areas of their habitat without actually defending them (see HABITAT). Such areas are known as home ranges. They often overlap with the home ranges of neighboring groups.

*See also* COMMUNAL ANIMALS.

## TERTIARY PERIOD (tûr′shē ĕr′ē pĭr′ē əd)

The Tertiary period is a division of the Cenozoic era that began about sixty-five million years ago and ended 1.64 million years ago. It is divided into five epochs: the Paleocene, Eocene, Oligocene, Miocene, and Pliocene (see EOCENE EPOCH; MIOCENE EPOCH; OLIGOCENE EPOCH; PALEOCENE EPOCH; PLIOCENE EPOCH).

Most of the giant reptiles were extinct at the beginning of the Tertiary period. Mammals developed into the main land creatures (see MAMMAL; REPTILE). Many mammals, including bats, camels, dogs, elephants, and horses, appeared during the Tertiary. Mammals reached the peak of their development during the Miocene epoch. The number of species has gradually decreased since then. Humanlike apes appeared toward the end of the Tertiary. The first humans appeared at the end of the period (see HUMAN BEING).

There was much sea life, and it was similar to today's sea life. Birds developed to their present state. Plant life was very modern by the end of the Tertiary. The Tertiary saw the building of the Alps and the Himalayas. The Tertiary climate was rather warm, though it began to cool off near the end. Much volcanic activity occurred during the Tertiary.

*See also* CENOZOIC ERA; GEOLOGICAL TIME SCALE; VOLCANO.

## TESLA, NIKOLA (1856–1943) (tĕs′ lə, nĭk′ ō lə)

Nikola Tesla was an electrical engineer who is most famous for his invention of the electric motor that

**NIKOLA TESLA—Inventor**

Nikola Tesla patented over 112 inventions, mostly electrical devices. He is most famous for the alternating-current (AC) electric motor. The SI unit of magnetic flux density is called the tesla in his honor.

uses alternating current (AC) (see ALTERNATING CURRENT; ELECTRIC MOTOR). Tesla was born in Smiljan, Croatia.

While a student at the University of Prague, Tesla became interested in electric motors. At that time, motors ran on direct current (DC) and used a device called a commutator to reverse the direction of the current. The direction of current in such a motor needs to be reversed to help make the part called the armature spin. This allows the electric motor to produce power. The commutator in direct current motors is inefficient because it leaks electricity (see COMMUTATOR; CURRENT, ELECTRIC; DIRECT CURRENT). Tesla designed a motor that did not need a commutator. His motor was based on alternating current, which reverses its direction on its own. Tesla's electric motor had coils built into the armature and another part of the electric motor called the stator. When AC passes through the coils in the stator, it generates a rotating magnetic field. By the process of induction, the magnetic field makes an electric current flow in the coils of the armature. This helps the armature spin (see INDUCTION).

By 1888, Tesla had moved to the United States and had received a patent on his alternating-current motor as well as patents on transformers and alternating-current generators. A patent is a document issued by a government. It grants a person exclusive rights to an invention for a period of time (see GENERATOR, ELECTRICAL; TRANSFORMER). Tesla's inventions were used to harness the power of Niagara Falls, a waterfall on the border of Canada and New York state. The mechanical energy of the water turned turbines (see TURBINE). The turbines in turn drove AC generators, which changed the mechanical energy into electricity. The transformer increased the voltage of the electricity to the point that it could be sent long distances over wires (see VOLT). This was the start of the modern electric power industry, in which alternating-current generators are used and alternating current is sent using transformers. Until that time, direct-current power plants were used. These plants could only deliver power over a few city blocks because they did not use transformers.

Tesla performed many experiments with electricity. He invented another transformer that had an air core rather than a metal core. This air core transformer is now called the Tesla coil. Today, the Tesla coil is being studied further and has been used experimentally by some scientists. Using his

**TESLA—Experiments**
Nikola Tesla sits reading amidst the huge sparks produced by the high-frequency coil alongside him. The photograph was taken in Colorado Springs, Colorado.

**TESLA—Hydroelectric power**

Tesla's inventions, including an alternating-current (AC) generator and a transformer, were used to harness the power of Niagara Falls to produce electricity. This was one of the first examples of hydroelectric power generation.

transformer, Tesla created artificial lightning (see LIGHTNING). He proved that the upper atmosphere was an excellent conductor of electricity (see ATMOSPHERE; CONDUCTION OF ELECTRICITY).

Tesla developed the first experimental wireless communication system before Guglielmo Marconi did (see MARCONI, GUGLIELMO). Guglielmo Marconi was later credited with inventing the wireless communication system we know today as radio (see RADIO). Scientists of the time, such as Marconi, limited their research to the part of the electromagnetic spectrum just above visible light. This part of the electromagnetic spectrum includes only very short waves (see ELECTROMAGNETIC RADIATION). Tesla, however, researched the entire spectrum. He correctly said that longer waves would be needed for wireless worldwide communication. Tesla also invented a device called an oscillator, which is used today in radio broadcasting (see OSCILLATOR).

Tesla invented the first fluorescent light (see ELECTRIC LIGHT). He also invented "wireless lights." His wireless lights were glass tubes that operated by induction from wires hidden in the ceiling of his laboratory.

During his lifetime, Tesla had many undeveloped ideas because he was not able to receive enough government or private funding. Also, after he died, his ideas could not be carried out because he had never made drawings or kept written plans. Instead, he had the unique ability to visualize his ideas to the tiniest detail. Tesla was granted over 112 U.S. patents and received many honors. In 1956, a museum was established in his honor in Belgrade, the capital of Serbia and the former capital of Yugoslavia. The museum houses much of his equipment.

Since the 1980s, a number of scientists and engineers have become interested in some of Tesla's undeveloped ideas. One of these ideas is to deliver electricity around the world without using wires. Scientists hope to use Tesla coil transformers to shoot electricity into the upper atmosphere. Because the upper atmosphere is highly conductive, wires would not be needed. Scientists also are developing Tesla's bladeless turbine. The bladeless turbine produces 60 percent more horsepower than conventional turbines (see HORSEPOWER). Also, the blades of conventional turbines are damaged by the action of the substance acting on them. Another area of Tesla's research that scientists are interested in is converting the drag produced by water or air flowing over a surface into additional energy (see AERODYNAMICS; DRAG). Scientists hope to apply this concept to pumps and nuclear reactors.

**TESTICLE** (tĕs′tĭ kəl) The testicles, or testes, are part of the male reproductive system. In humans, they are a pair of small, egg-shaped organs located between the penis and the anus in a sac called the scrotum. When a boy reaches puberty, the pituitary gland begins releasing special sex hormones. These hormones cause the testicles to develop and mature (see HORMONE; PUBERTY; REPRODUCTIVE SYSTEM).

The testicles produce the male gametes (sex cells) known as sperm. They also produce a male sex hormone, testosterone. The testicles contain thousands of tiny, coiled tubes called seminiferous tubules. It is in these tubules that millions of sperm are produced and mature each day. Sperm are moved through the seminiferous tubules and stored in the epididymis, an enlarged tube that rests on the top of each testicle.
*See also* REPRODUCTION.

**TEST TUBE BABY** A test tube baby is a baby who is born normally, but who grew from an egg cell taken from the mother's body and artificially united with a sperm cell in a laboratory. The fertilized egg cell (called an embryo) grows in the laboratory until it has divided into eight cells. Then it is introduced into the mother's womb (uterus) so that it can implant itself in the uterine wall and develop normally (see EMBRYO; FERTILIZATION; IMPLANTATION; PREGNANCY; REPRODUCTION; REPRODUCTIVE SYSTEM). Another name for this process is *in vitro* fertilization. It was first used successfully in England in 1978. *In vitro* fertilization is used only with women who cannot become

pregnant any other way and after the couple have undergone extensive tests to see why they cannot have children. The ability to fertilize human egg cells artificially has raised fears that they would be used for experiments, but there are strict ethical codes and laws to prevent this.

**TETANUS** (tĕt′n əs) Tetanus is a deadly disease that affects muscles. It is also called lockjaw because it causes severe muscular spasms (contractions) of the jaw. These spasms make it hard for the victim to open his or her mouth (see DISEASE; MUSCLE).

Tetanus is caused by toxins (poisons) that are produced by certain bacteria (see BACTERIA). These bacteria live in dust and dirt and need no air to survive. They get into the body through breaks in the skin, such as cuts and other wounds. That is why it is extremely important to clean any cuts and wounds quickly.

Symptoms of tetanus usually start to appear from five to fifteen days after the bacteria enter the body. By then, the poison has spread through the bloodstream to the muscles. The victim feels depressed, has headaches, and has trouble opening his or her mouth or swallowing. After a while, muscular spasms in other body muscles begin to interfere with breathing. If the patient is not treated, he or she may die.

Persons can be immunized easily against tetanus. This immunity lasts for several years. If an unimmunized person develops the disease, doctors treat it with antitoxin injections. In some cases, however, this treatment does not work.
*See also* ANTITOXIN; IMMUNITY.

**TETRAETHYL LEAD** (tĕt′rə ĕth′əl lĕd) Tetraethyl lead, $(C_2H_5)_4Pb$, is a poisonous, colorless liquid. It is an antiknock agent and may be added to gasoline to help prevent knocking. The exhaust from tetraethyl lead contains poisonous lead compounds that pollute the air (see COMPOUND; POLLUTION). Because of this, tetraethyl lead has been phased out of most gasoline. Most of the cars on the road today use unleaded gasoline.
*See also* GASOLINE; LEAD.